The Terry Lectures

AERONAUTICS AT THE MID-CENTURY

By Jerome C. Hunsaker

Professor of Aeronautical Engineering

Massachusetts Institute of Technology

AERONAUTICS

London: Geoffrey Cumberlege, Oxford University Press

at the Mid-Century

New Haven: YALE UNIVERSITY PRESS, **1952**

THE DWIGHT HARRINGTON TERRY FOUNDATION LECTURES ON

RELIGION IN THE LIGHT OF SCIENCE AND PHILOSOPHY

This volume is based upon the twenty-eighth series of lectures delivered at Yale University on the Foundation established by the late Dwight H. Terry of Bridgeport, Connecticut, through his gift of $100,000 as an endowment fund for the delivery and subsequent publication of "Lectures on Religion in the Light of Science and Philosophy."

The deed of gift declares that "the object of this Foundation is not the promotion of scientific investigation and discovery, but rather the assimilation and interpretation of that which has been or shall be hereafter discovered, and its application to human welfare, especially by the building of the truths of science and philosophy into the structure of a broadened and purified religion. The founder believes that such a religion will greatly stimulate intelligent effort for the improvement of human conditions and the advancement of the race in strength and excellence of character. To this end it is desired that lectures or a series of lectures be given by men eminent in their respective departments, on ethics, the history of civilization and religion, biblical research, all sciences and branches of knowledge which have an important bearing on the subject, all the great laws of nature, especially of evolution . . . also such interpretations of literature and sociology as are in accord with the spirit of this Foundation, to the end that the Christian spirit may be nurtured in the fullest light of the world's knowledge and that mankind may be helped to attain its highest possible welfare and happiness upon this earth . . .

"The lectures shall be subject to no philosophical or religious test and no one who is an earnest seeker after truth shall be excluded because his views seem radical or destructive of existing beliefs. The founder realizes that the liberalism of one generation is often conservatism in the next, and that many an apostle of true liberty has suffered martyrdom at the hands of the orthodox. He therefore lays special emphasis on complete freedom of utterance, and would welcome expressions of conviction from sincere thinkers of differing standpoints even when these may run counter to the generally accepted views of the day. The founder stipulates only that the managers of the fund shall be satisfied that the lecturers are well qualified for their work and are in harmony with the cardinal principles of the Foundation, which are loyalty to the truth, lead where it will, and devotion to human welfare."

PREFACE

Human flight is a technical innovation of this century with great social and political effects that are now becoming apparent. Before flight was possible, men dreamed of the conquest of the air as an ultimate good. Later, the realization of air power suggested to some an easy conquest of the world; and now the need has become felt of a world organization for mutual security against air-borne aggression.

Geography has hitherto compartmented peoples by means of the physical features of land and sea, by climate zones and cultural frontiers. Now we have mobility in a third dimension with which to reckon with geography. The ocean of air provides highways from anywhere to everywhere. Geographical boundaries, largely determined by the older modes of transportation, are becoming unreal; they no longer give security or prevent the interpenetration of ideas. An iron curtain is an artificial and socially expensive attempt to maintain a geographical status more appropriate to a previous century.

In this book I wish to examine the possibilities of utilizing this third dimension and to demonstrate that the good or evil of the new mobility depends on the adjustments society makes to human flight. The first chapter discusses the state of technology from which the Wright Brothers' invention arose and outlines the subsequent development of that invention. The next describes the present state of the art of aeronautics, principally as it applies to air transportation, with some speculation about apparent limitations and where evident trends may lead. The last chapter has to do with the impact of both civil and military aeronautics on our society.

JEROME C. HUNSAKER

CONTENTS

LIST OF ILLUSTRATIONS

AERONAUTICS AT THE MID-CENTURY

The only photograph taken of man's first flight, Kitty Hawk, N.C., December 17, 1903. The plane, piloted by Orville Wright, has just taken off from the monorail. Wilbur Wright, running at the side, held the wing to balance the machine until it left the track.

I. FIFTY YEARS OF DEVELOPMENT

Human flight occurred for the first time in the history of our race on December 17, 1903—less than a half century ago. In the years since then we have witnessed the progressive conquest of the air. Every person alive today is affected by it. There is a change in our relation to distant places and peoples; the air presents a clear route between us and them, a route for trade and the interchange of visits and ideas. It can also be the path of sudden destruction, for air power reaching into the interior of a continent or to formerly isolated islands gives a new and frightening weapon to an aggressor.

3

Macaulay wrote in 1830: "We are told that our age has invented atrocities beyond the imagination of our fathers, that society has been brought into a state compared with which extermination would be a blessing." And Whitehead a century later: "The world is now faced with a self-evolving system, which it cannot stop. . . . It is obvious that the gain in material power affords opportunity for social betterment. . . . But material power in itself is ethically neutral. It can equally work in the wrong direction. . . . We must expect, therefore, that the future will disclose dangers. It is the business of the future to be dangerous; . . . In the immediate future there will be less security than in the immediate past, less stability . . . on the whole, the great ages have been unstable ages."[1]

These times are indeed dangerous. With the divided world in its present state of strain, one could even wish there were no airplanes—at least none to deliver atom bombs. Yet it is the threat of the atom bomb that should impel nations to prudence and common sense, just as dread of the Last Judgment has impelled individuals to good behavior.

Historically one might liken the development of the airplane, with its effects in both peace and war, to the domestication of the horse. On the one hand, the horse gave mobility to men and their goods and, with roads and carts, permitted society to evolve into larger national groups. On the other hand, hordes of Mongol horsemen swarmed over immense areas of Asia and Europe and threatened the extinction of civilization.

[1] Alfred North Whitehead, *Science and the Modern World* (New York, Macmillan, 1925), pp. 295, 298-299.

4

Again, there may be a parallel with ships. In the Mediterranean Phoenicians, Greeks, and Romans developed sea power for trade and colonization as well as for war and pillage. The Vikings' ships enabled them to dominate northern Europe and Iceland and to establish cod and herring fishing. The sea power of Elizabethan England, under Drake and Frobisher and Raleigh, led to an immense expansion of overseas enterprise. English merchants traded with new and distant markets. In Trevelyan's words: "Corresponding to the change of markets was the change of mental outlook. . . . Englishmen looked forward to new things. . . . The actual achievement of the reign in Atlantic sea power and exploration made ready the path for the folk-wandering of the English people that began in the next generation."[2]

The seaworthy vessels that conquered the Atlantic also made successful war on the Spanish and Dutch. Superior ships and seamen were backed by a nation at a peak of wealth and adventurous spirit. The golden age of Elizabeth and Shakespeare came to full flower with the opening of the sea as a universal highway.

Thus it is evident that when a radical change in means of transportation arrives, exploitation of the new mobility produces social and economic changes, including those resulting from war and conquest.

The airplane is relatively new, but air power has already profoundly affected the outcome of a great war and still constitutes a threat to the security of the victorious allies. In its civil application, however, the airplane has yet to

[2] G. M. Trevelyan, *Illustrated English Social History* (London, Longmans, Green, 1950), 2, 51, 52.

attain its potential world-wide utilization. But air transport has arrived, and is growing as fast as political, economic, and technical conditions permit.

Human flight has obsessed the imagination from earliest times. The Psalmists wondered at the way of an eagle in the air. There are winged figures in Assyrian art, Greek legends of flying chariots, Sinbad the Sailor and the great Roc, the witch in Macbeth with her broomstick, and medieval representations of flying angels. Most of these aerial navigators were somewhat miraculous, but perhaps no more so than the twenty-foot pterodactyl of paleontology which Sir George Greenhill[3] estimated to require for its flight an atmosphere of much greater density than ours.

As early as 1783 the Montgolfier brothers sailed with the wind in a balloon. In 1785 Dr. John Jeffries, a Boston physician, reported to the Royal Society of London the first crossing of the English Channel by himself and J. P. Blanchard, a French balloonist. After this, 124 years had to pass before the first airplane crossing. But bold adventurers leaped from high places with parachutes. Lilienthal, the German pioneer, in the latter part of the 19th century succeeded in gliding from hill to valley on man-made wings, making some 2,000 glides before his fatal crash. And his gliders had good stability and sustaining power although inadequate control.

The airplane as a structure was described in 1809 by Sir George Cayleigh,[4] who explained how to make a sur-

---

[3] *The Dynamics of Mechanical Flight* (New York, Van Nostrand, 1912), p. 4.

[4] *Nicholson's Journal*, London, 1809-10.

(Left) Montgolfier hot air balloon, 1783

(Right) Dr. John Jeffries of Boston in the balloon in which he crossed the English Channel, 1785.

(Below) Lilienthal glider, 1893

face support a weight by the application of power to the resistance of the air. He speculated on whether James Watt's steam engine might some day be used to fly a machine in the air.

In 1842 Henson,[5] another Englishman, patented a monoplane with a steam engine, two propellers, and provided with vertical and horizontal rudders to steer it. After Cayleigh, Henson, as nearly as any one person, foretold the flying machine. All essential elements were disclosed except means for lateral control.

Even this element was somewhat dimly foreseen by Mouillard[6] who in 1881 described the soaring flight of vultures and the twisting of their wings to maintain lateral balance. Probably the principle of the warping wing could have been patented at any time after that, but no one claimed it and there was no real reason to do so. Human flight was too formidable a project for the 19th century. True flight had to wait for a light engine.

Experimenters continued to study the reaction of the air to moving objects. Phillips[7] measured the force of the air on models of cambered wings in what was probably the first wind tunnel. Eiffel[8] dropped objects from his beautiful iron tower in Paris to determine from the rate of fall their resistance to the air. Langley measured the

[5.] British patent No. 9478.

[6.] Louis P. Mouillard, *L'Empire de l'air; essai d'ornithologie appliquée à l'aviation* (Paris, 1881).

[7.] Horatio Phillips, "Experiments with Currents of Air," *Engineering*, London, Aug. 14, 1885, pp. 161, 162.

[8.] G. Eiffel, *Travaux scientifiques exécutés à la tour de 300 mètres de 1889 à 1900* (Paris, Maretheux, 1900).

8

forces on model wings on a whirling arm and flew perfectly stable model airplanes over the Potomac River[9].

The simultaneous advent of gasoline and the motorcar with the internal combustion engine in the closing years of the 19th century suggested to Langley and other experimenters the application of an engine and propeller to a glider to make a true flying machine. They were all unsuccessful in achieving a practical flying machine because the principle of control in flight was lacking. Clement Ader in France was observed by witnesses to leave the ground in his steam-driven *avion* for short hops—at least the tracks on the grass were interrupted. But Ader's machine like Henson's had no lateral control. Maxim in England spent a fortune on a great steam-driven airplane tethered to rails. The machine left the rails, indicating sustentation, but it did not fly. It too had no lateral control.

By the beginning of our century all the components of the airplane, including the gasoline engine, had become known. Yet the elusive combination needed for a practical vehicle was still to be discovered. Alexander Graham Bell and his friend Langley were confident that the key to the riddle would soon be found. Perhaps it was not found sooner because flying models had been misleadingly successful. By careful adjustment of fins and by raising the wing tips, such craft were made inherently stable and appeared to fly by themselves very well with no need for controls.

[9.] S. P. Langley, *Experiments in Aerodynamics* (Smithsonian Institution, Washington, D. C., 1891).

Langley aerodrome of 1903 as reconstructed and with floats added.
Flown at Lake Keuka, N.Y., in 1914

Lanchester[10] made a brilliant analysis of the inherent stability of model airplanes in 1897, long before there were real airplanes. His work was a little like a treatise on the dynamics of the automobile before any automobile existed. The Physical Society of London declined to print this paper, but some thirty years later Lanchester was awarded a gold medal for it by the Royal Aeronautical Society.

Eventually the key to the riddle of airplane control was found by the Wright brothers,[11] and with great persistence and true scientific intuition they developed their successful flying machine of the 1903 Kitty Hawk flights. It is highly probable that the Wrights were not conscious of the world-shaking significance in the first proof that their plans for an airplane were practical. As evidence we have the telegram Orville sent his father: "Success; Four flights Thursday morning: Started from level with engine power alone: Average speed 31 miles: Longest 59 seconds: Inform Press: Home Christmas: Orville." The press did not think a flight of less than a minute worth reporting.

It might be pleasant for Americans to think that the Wright brothers invented the airplane in a flash of genius and so realized the age-old dream of human flight, but this would be to capture only a portion of truth. However, the Wrights were the first men to fly and they did devise and use practical means for controlling an airplane in pitch,

[10.] F. W. Lanchester, *Aerodynamics* (2d ed. London, Constable, 1909).

[11.] U. S. patent No. 821,393, issued May 22, 1906.

roll, and yaw. Had they not succeeded, it now seems certain that someone else soon would have. In 1900 men had confidence that desired effects could be had by finding the appropriate cause. The physical world seemed a mechanism to be manipulated. Nothing seemed impossible, not even flying through the air. The time was ripe, the incentive great, and the basic concepts of the airplane and its propulsion existed. Furthermore, at the beginning of the century American enterprise was accelerating after the Spanish war. Enthusiasm for new ideas ran high. Applied science had been producing successive marvels: the telephone, electric light and power, alloy steels and aluminum, and finally gasoline and the automobile. Young men like the Wright brothers naturally turned from bicycles toward something more exciting.

The enormous development of aeronautics in our lifetime is a consequence of the availability of gasoline. The Wright brothers' invention at any previous time could have amounted to no more than an improvement in gliders, perhaps of some interest to sportsmen. Before 1900 petroleum supplied liniment, lamp oil, and lubricants with, as an unwelcome by-product, some benzenes and napthas of no value. In January of 1900 the world's first great oil gusher was blown in near Beaumont, Texas, spouting an estimated 100,000 barrels a day before it could be brought under control. Nothing like Spindletop had ever been seen before. A granite shaft now marks the place, inscribed, with true Texas appreciation: "On this spot on the tenth day of the twentieth century a new era in civilization began." After Spindletop, oil became an industry and opened possibilities for the machine age that brought about rapid changes in western society. There was

12

now abundant energy to run automobiles and airplanes. In ten years the oil production of the nation tripled, in another ten years it doubled again, to a million barrels a day. Today it is more than six million barrels daily.

The airplane was born into a time of both abundant energy from oil and growing political instability. The 19th century closed with the Boer war and the Spanish-American war; the 20th century opened with the Russo-Japanese war and soon saw the first World War. Great states

Bleriot, first airplane to cross the English Channel, 1909

were changing in relative power and were strained by economic pressures. It is no wonder that the airplane was at once taken up for intensive development by countries that foresaw its possibilities in future conflict. France, Germany, Britain, the United States, Russia, Italy, and Japan established organizations for military and naval aviation. Private enterprise was encouraged to develop the new machine. Prizes and trophies were put up for international competition.

In 1909 Louis Bleriot flew across the English Channel, winning the London *Daily Mail* £1000 prize and marking the breaching of the sea ramparts of Britain for all time. The Gordon Bennett and then the Schneider Cup international races stimulated designers and pilots to strive for speed. World's records were broken annually. Speed races became so costly that sportsmen withdrew from them and governments took over, with entrants from their armed services. Following World War I, the Atlantic and then the Pacific were conquered by daring aviators.

Along with the serious concern of governments with the rapid development of aviation went great public interest in flying, and consequent waste of lives. Aviation was naturally exciting and popular. Small boys wore their caps with visor to the rear like the Wrights. Associations of aviation enthusiasts gave themselves dinners and presented trophies to selected aviators for doing something for the first time or for doing it quicker.

Nevertheless, competition was to produce results. The British Spitfire fighter with its Rolls-Royce engine, the Merlin, which in the hands of intrepid young flyers won the Battle of Britain, was a direct development from the

14

Royal Air Force entry in the Schneider Cup race of a previous year.

The Wright airplane had a sustaining wing structure, engine-driven propeller, and means for controlling attitude in pitch, roll, and yaw. This basic type has continued to the present day. Its performance was rapidly improved by application of the advancing technology of the new century. Research and development were stimulated by generous national subventions, and two wars poured billions into the production of bigger and better flying machines.

British Spitfire airplane, 1940

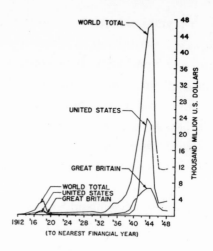

Expenditures on aeronautics, world-wide

In his 1950 Wilbur Wright Memorial Lecture,[12] Sir Richard Fairey examined world-wide government expenditure on aeronautics making intricate allowances for the shrinking values of money and varying exchange rates. He showed that expenditures were relatively modest during the first part of the period between wars, but that the world total rose abruptly into the billions between 1934 and 1939. His analysis stopped with 1948, by which time the total expenditure on aeronautics by all nations in peace and war, since the Wright brothers made their contribution to the technology of transportation, added up to 256 billion U. S. dollars.

Orville Wright was not unaware of the military value of the airplane, since his first sale in 1908 was to the United States War Department. However, he always con-

[12.] *The Journal of the Royal Aeronautical Society,* London, *54,* July 1950, 408-430.

tended that he and his brother Wilbur thought of their airplane first as a contribution to international communications, trade, and good will. It is conceivable that the next fifty years will prove him right in the long run.

Inventors were at first the designers; then engineers and scientists took over. The demands of the airplane led to the creation of strong light alloys, high-octane gasoline, and high-output engines, as well as special operating equipment using radio, radar, and autopilots. A new science of aerodynamics was evolved to serve designers. New impulses were given to the classical but somewhat sterile theories of hydrodynamics, elasticity, gyroscopics, and navigation. Old ideas for a gas turbine were resurrected and applied with spectacular success to jet propulsion.

Taking speed records of propeller-driven airplanes as a measure of progress, the increase in forty-seven years has been from about 40 to nearly 500 mph, or at a rate of some 10 miles per year of effort. Simply projecting this trend suggests that it would take the next fifty years to bring the speed record to 1,000 mph. Yet the newspapers inform us that jet-propelled research airplanes have repeatedly flown at supersonic speeds, or more than 1,000 mph already. Examination of the jet-propelled airplane shows that it is not the airplane of the Wright brothers; something revolutionary has been added. The radically lighter and more powerful means of propulsion, eliminating the propeller, is a mutation that upsets the trend of statistics of past growth. The piston-engine propeller-driven airplane has indeed made a normal growth curve, topping off between 1940 and 1950, with a maximum sea-level speed below 500 mph.

The performance of jet-propelled airplanes is too recent

17

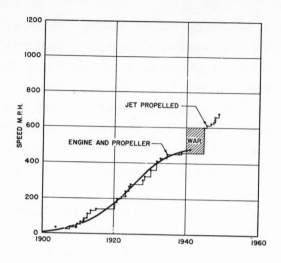

World's speed records

to establish a trend from which to venture a forecast. All we know is that we have to do with a new kind of airplane to which vastly increased thrust can be applied. How fast will it go? The answer seems to be: as fast as required.

The limits on useful speed will be imposed by practical considerations. Extreme speed can be attained only with a high rate of fuel consumption, even when advantage is taken of the diminished resistance of the air at high altitudes. Higher speed means shorter range or the sacrifice of payload. Furthermore, wings may be clipped to a degree that makes control for take-off and landing impractical. Pushing possibilities to the limit, one can replace the pilot by automatic or robot controls, launch by catapult or from another airplane, and expend at the end of flight. Such an ephemeral insect-like thing is the guided missile, featured by the popular press but otherwise clothed in security wrappings. Twelve-ton German missiles, rocket-propelled for less than a minute, landed in London with a ton of explosive from a launching point in France; their velocity exceeded 3,000 mph over part of the trajectory. And a recent naval test rocket is reported to have been sent to an altitude of 135 miles.

We already use rockets for exploring the upper air, for accelerated take-off of airplanes, and for other auxiliary purposes; no doubt further uses will appear. Since rockets are relatively extravagant of fuel, they seem likely to find their best applications to weapons. Present military uses include rocket weapons as armament for airplanes, combat vehicles, and vessels. Such rockets are effective as substitutes for guns when launched with proper fire control, although their accuracy is inferior to that of a gun.

Long-range rocket-propelled missiles are under intensive development both here and abroad, the incentive being to take advantage of the possibility of guiding them to the target by means of radio or radar. Such guided missiles may be either ground- or air-launched and directed against either ground or air targets. The proximity fuse, perfected by Americans during the last war, makes a direct hit on a hostile aircraft unnecessary. A near passage is enough to explode the missile.

Use of rockets for military purposes will no doubt continue, with substantial improvements in frightfulness over the German models. Even engineers have contributed to public anxiety by dreaming up projects for inter-

19

NACA research rocket, Wallops Island, Va., 1950

continental atomic rockets, satellite vehicles circling the earth like moons, and space ships for interplanetary excursions. The *New York Tribune* has been moved to exclaim: "The rocket's red glare is now seen on every battlefield, and even more on every testing ground casting revolutionary implications for many forms of warfare with its lurid light."[13]

The convergence of the technology of rocket propulsion with electronic guidance gives certainty to the prediction of aerial vehicles and missiles of greatly enhanced performance, but practical useful results will be delayed until many associated technical problems are solved. For example, extreme speed through the air raises the skin temperature of a missile beyond that tolerable by ordinary construction materials, to say nothing of the delicate instruments carried within the missile. At extreme altitudes there is so little air that steering by rudders is impractical. For a manned vehicle, there remains the problem of supporting life under extremely unfavorable conditions and, finally, of bringing the vehicle safely back to rest on the ground. All of these problems stimulate research, but research into unknown regions is an adventure for which no time schedule can be set.

The inherent limitation in range of any aircraft propelled by chemical fuel might be overcome by nuclear power. The prospect of a nuclear-powered airplane is foreseen by Gordon Dean, Chairman of the Atomic Energy Commission, in his testimony before a House Appropriations subcommittee. He is quoted as saying:[14] "I think in the next decade

13. *New York Tribune,* Aug. 9, 1951.

14. *New York Times,* Oct. 8, 1951.

21

you will probably have a plane in the air the power for which comes from a reactor. . . . I think you would have the beginning of an atomic Air Force within a decade." More recently[15] Major General D. L. Putt, U.S.A.F., has written: "I think we can safely predict a nuclear-powered aircraft capable of flying around the world at supersonic speed without refueling and under complete automatic control."

Progress toward a mobile nuclear power plant must be substantial, as the Navy has already contracted for the first nuclear-powered submarine, and nuclear-powered airplanes are on order.

A speculative calculation can be made to show that a few pounds of fissionable material might suffice for an "escape rocket" to leave the earth. This idea shifts the problem from the source of power to the means to apply it. The nuclear energy must be transferred to a working fluid, such as hydrogen, to be ejected at high velocity. The material that can withstand the temperature involved is unknown, and the engineering data which are necessary for the development of a practical design are not available for scrutiny.

Technical progress obviously limits air power, but only the combination of quality and quantity gives superiority at a given time. In the last war this country took an uncalculated risk, to concentrate on conventional aircraft, and won, but largely because of two unusual factors that may not be present in future. These were, first, the fact that we entered the war after the Battle of Britain had been won by the Royal Air Force and, second, that Hitler misman-

[15] "Trends in Air Force Research and Development" *S.A.E. Journal,* March 1952, p. 43.

aged German technical resources and made the wrong allocations of technical effort.

Nevertheless, the Germans came up with a few jet-propelled fighters and a lot of rocket-propelled missiles in the last year of the war. Had they done this two years earlier, when really intensive production was still possible in their heavily bombed country, they might well have seized command of the air and given the war an entirely different course. We escaped having to continue an exhausting and bloody struggle while we changed our concept of what would win and proceeded to develop the necessary equipment and tactics. We won with overwhelming numbers of excellent standardized airplanes of types under development at the beginning of the war, but continuously improved in performance and striking power during the war.

As a result of a decision at the highest level, the national research effort was concentrated on the improvement of aircraft in the production program. This meant that research was restricted to what could be completed quickly and applied to help win that war, not some future one. From 1941 to 1945 there was little scientific manpower to spare for fundamental investigations. The national research program was about 90% specific development problems and 10% basic research to gain needed knowledge.

As I have said, a risk was taken, and the success of this short-range policy must not mislead us in future. It is almost a historical axiom that preparations for a possible future war tend to be patterned on events and alleged lessons of the last one. Yet when the new war comes everything is sure to be different: geography, objectives, weapons, and strategy.

Also, it is an axiom of mass production that designs must be "frozen" to achieve quantity output, at least for substantial periods of time. American thinking is predisposed to freezing standard designs for production. Yet it would be a dangerous mistake to apply such a policy rigidly to our current build-up of air power. We cannot afford to limit our efforts to what can tide us over the present crisis and to stockpile current airplanes. The best authorities and our judgment tell us that we face an indefinite period of international tension.

For air power, quality and quantity must go together. Research must stimulate and guide technical progress and keep a good distance ahead of a potential enemy. Research can be continuous, while development of new designs proceeds step by step on a type basis. In this way industry can be kept ready to produce the most effective aircraft, when required by events. We also have responsibilities that oblige us to provide technical leadership to our allies.

So far as paper work goes, we seem now to have made the right decisions and are beginning to implement them. In March 1946 a policy was adopted which assigned aeronautical research to the National Advisory Committee for Aeronautics, design and development to the aeronautical industry, and testing and evaluation to the Armed Services. The NACA's three laboratories have been enlarged in staff and facilities. The industry has been almost overwhelmed with orders for new aircraft and is setting up vastly enlarged manufacturing plants. The Armed Services are building new and larger proving grounds and test centers.

This is all very costly but necessary. The research effort is justified because there is so much to learn about new phenomena at the higher speeds made possible by jet and rocket propulsion. Designers need reliable engineering data before new aircraft and missiles of superior performance can be created. The industry must have adequate plants and tools for production, and finally the Armed Services must test, evaluate, and select their equipment to meet changing requirements for aerial warfare. Progress in the development of postwar types of airplane has been excellent, and there is no doubt that their quantity production is justified, as the first step in the build-up of our air power.

I leave out of this discussion design trends in military airplanes. The design of military airplanes, like that of warships, is governed largely by the foreign policy and military plans of the nation, checked by intelligence of actual or potential foreign equipment, and controlled by the general state of technology at a given time.

The international situation for the next fifty years is of course unpredictable. At the moment there is an evident trend toward preparation for war. Aeronautical development is therefore directed toward the needs of national security, but it should be kept in mind that technical advances in military aeronautics are ultimately applicable to civil uses. We have twice observed the stimulating effect of war on postwar air transportation. Research results, as they disclose new knowledge, suggest to designers in a competitive industry new solutions. From their experiments come practical improvements, usually minor, but over the years their effect is cumulative.

The trends of technical progress are usually evident from a comparison of current designs with research data not yet applied. There is always a time lag before research findings come into general use, but current trends justify only short-range predictions, perhaps over a ten-year rather than a fifty-year period.

For example, it is evident that the gas turbine is revolutionary in its effect of affording more power and hence higher speed to modern airplanes. The reciprocating engine is mature, and efforts to improve it have reached a stage of diminishing returns. The gas turbine is simpler, lighter, and more compact. Its big disadvantage is its youth, and consequent occasional unreliability and a tendency to extravagance. Youth will be outgrown and hence one may safely predict that reliability and economy will be established. The fuel economy is now relatively poor, but three ways to improve it are known.

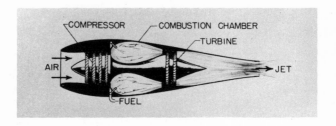

Turbo-jet propulsion system

First, and most readily, better fuel economy can come from higher compression of the combustion air. A current compression ratio of four to one can be raised to eight or even twelve to one by using more powerful compressors. The design principles for such compressors are now established. Early application should bring turbine fuel economy at high cruising speeds down to equal that of the piston engine.

26

Second, running turbines hotter will improve both fuel economy and power output. The current limit on allowable temperature is determined by the metals available. Research indicates the possibility of better heat-resisting metals and ceramics. Furthermore, experimental schemes for turbine-blade cooling indicate interesting possibilities for raising gas temperatures with present blade materials. Eventual success with higher temperature will bring substantial gains.

Third, it is known that better economy can be had by the use of heat exchanger surfaces to transfer some waste heat from the exhaust to the compressed air for combustion. This together with other improvements should make it possible to attain a fuel economy superior to that of any previously known aircraft power plant. However, heat exchangers will not be adopted quickly. They involve increased weight and space, and a complexity that threatens reliability and ease of maintenance. Perhaps marine and stationary gas turbines will pioneer this avenue.

I believe that the propeller is the simplest and most efficient machine for converting torque to thrust. It is man's invention; it is not found in nature. If the gas turbine is such a superior power plant, it is a natural idea to gear it to a propeller to make it more effective than when its exhaust jet alone is used to give thrust.

The high-velocity jet is certainly a simple method of propulsion, and it weighs nothing; but it is wasteful at low airplane speeds. The kinetic energy of the jet is all lost; only its momentum gives thrust. The propeller also creates a jet in its slip stream, but this is a large low-velocity jet in which the ratio of momentum (thrust) to kinetic energy is high. Good propellers have an efficiency as high as 88%.

Over the years the speed of commercial air transports has lagged behind the airplane speed records by fifteen or twenty years. When the speed record was 400 mph, air transports cruised at 200. Now the new transports cruise at better than 300 mph. As military experience with high-speed flight accumulates, we may expect the speed of air transports to follow with a conservative lag but probably not so great as in the past.

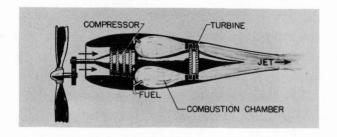

Turbo-prop propulsion system

It has long been considered that propellers become inefficient at an airplane speed of much over 400 mph. However, recent research suggests a change in propeller design which should render propellers effective beyond 500 mph and perhaps to 600. There are practical difficulties to be overcome, but discounting them it appears that the gas turbine driving a propeller promises the more powerful drive needed to get higher transport speed while retaining the high efficiency of the propeller. The prediction of the early appearance of faster air transports with geared turbine-propeller drive is easy.

28

That in a more distant future there will be reason to fly passengers at supersonic speeds seems doubtful. There certainly will be good reason for bombers to fly at the maximum speed the art permits. When they do, propellers cannot be used and jets will take over. When air transport wishes to emulate the speed of bombers, it too will have to use jet propulsion.

In the present state of knowledge, considerations of economy favor the propeller-turbine power plant for long nonstop routes. For routes with stops at 1,000-mile intervals, the advantages of extra speed may be controlling, and jet propulsion used. For feeder-line and local service, and for freight and general utility work, the propeller and reciprocating engine seem best.

Any engineer will agree, I think, that each of the different means of propulsion will be used in future wherever there is a real advantage. Research and development may change their relative merits from time to time, and unpredictable inventions may occur. Just now it appears that the gas turbine has good possibilities for substantial improvement, whether used for jet propulsion or to drive a propeller.

There has been a continuous rise in air transport speeds for the last twenty-five years. The British jet-propelled transports, Comet and Jetliner, promise continuation of the secular speed increase we have been accustomed to. I have no reason to project the straight line of civil airplane speeds to intersect 1,000 mph in 1970. This would be to enter the region of transonic speed where new kinds of aerodynamic trouble can be predicted.

Air transport cannot proceed at once to exploit all the possibilities of the art suggested by current research. A

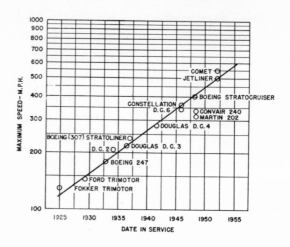

Speed of air transports

number of difficult problems must first find practical solutions. The public is conditioned to expect uninterrupted progress, but trees do not grow to the sky. There are always limitations in any art, either permanent in physical laws or temporary due to the current state of technology. Furthermore, progress is stopped at times by a realization of diminishing returns from more effort along conventional lines. The difficult practical problems that face air transportation will no doubt eventually find acceptable solutions, but the timing is uncertain.

One might ask where are the inherent physical limitations to further progress and whether we are now approaching diminishing returns for our effort. Should we wait for research to clarify the unknown before aeronautical engineers proceed further, or should we urge the engineers to proceed boldly and to let research later find the cause of failures? In time of war the bold advance may be justified, but it can be costly in lives and in confidence.

30

Good answers to many of these questions are not now available. Public support led to a poor trail in the case of the hydrogen-filled Zeppelins. The unwarranted and disastrous expansion of airplane manufacturing in 1929 was hardly a false start, but it was premature. The promoters had a good idea, but the airplanes were not then commercially useful. That seems to have been an example of unregulated private enterprise that resulted in financial rather than technical damage. The Securities and Exchange Commission has since been established and it should help to prevent such abuses of public confidence.

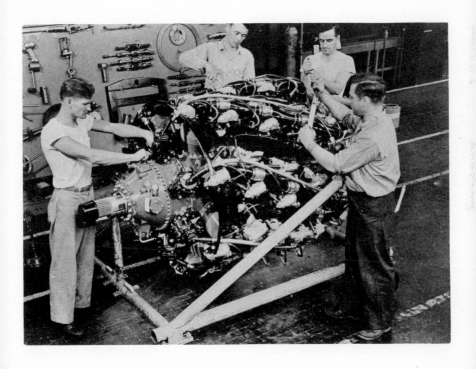

28-cylinder Wasp Major

An example of diminishing returns relative to effort is furnished by the multicylinder aircraft engine. Following, and usually leading, the general advance of the automotive art, the aircraft engine has been developed in fifty years to a peak of efficiency, with an output of some 4,000 horsepower, a weight of less than one pound per horsepower, and a fuel consumption of less than one-half pound per horsepower hour. This has come about by the grouping of as many as twenty-eight cylinders about a compact crank case with intricate ignition leads, valve mechanisms, and fuel, air, and exhaust plumbing nested about it. Small improvements are still possible, of course, by refinement, but most improvements appear to involve increased weight. Such engines can be raised somewhat in power output but there is a limiting factor that makes such gains increasingly difficult to achieve. The power developed varies as the volume of a cylinder, while the heat dissipated in cooling depends on the area of the walls. Cylinders cannot be run much hotter with existing metals and lubricants and therefore cannot be made larger with advantage. To get more power more cylinders are required and more complication.

The conclusion is that the aircraft piston engine is mature and a radical increase in output is not to be had, regardless of the expense and effort put on it.

Consideration of the power needed for very high speed leads to the idea that there is a physical limitation to the speed of the present type of airplane due to the compressibility of the air. Near the speed of sound, the air offers very greatly increased resistance to the passage of an airplane; it fails to move aside as the plane advances. Shock or compression waves are formed which destroy the smooth flow over the wings, changing the aerodynamic forces in magnitude and distribution. As a result, the airplane may become unbalanced, get out of control, or even disintegrate under severe buffeting.

One can say, from what is known now, that conventional airplanes with conventional engines are limited for practical use to speeds well below the speed of sound (750 mph at sea level). The piston engine has not enough power to push to such a speed, and the conventional airplane could not be flown there even if enough power were applied.

NACA supersonic airfoil. Shadow photograph at air speed 50% beyond the velocity of sound, showing shock wave at leading edge

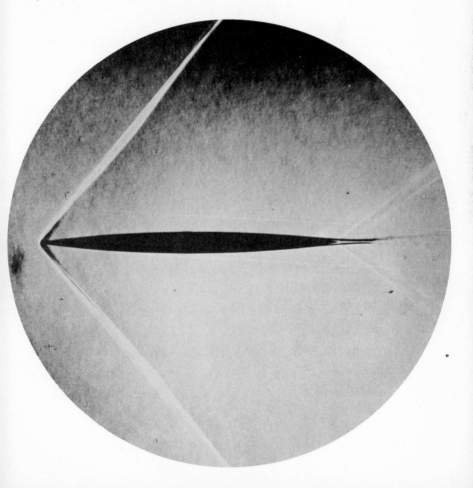

NACA supersonic wing-body combination. Research model mounted in wind tunnel at Ames Aeronautical Laboratory, Moffet Field, Calif.

Actually, there is no absolute sonic barrier. Jet-propulsion gas turbines can give power enough, and modern aerodynamic research has shown how to shape wings and bodies to be flown safely through the sonic range of speeds and into the supersonic. There is, of course, an increase in fuel consumption at such speeds but not to the prohibitive degree that would be the case for an airplane of conventional form.

Here we have an answer to the question as to the relative precedence of research and bold experiment. Bold experimenters might have tried for supersonic flight as soon as jet propulsion was available, but they would not have survived enough experiments to learn anything from their experience. Without the guidance of aerodynamic research, supersonic flight would not have been achieved experimentally today.

Supersonic research airplane, Douglas Skyrocket

II. AIR TRANSPORTATION

I have attempted in the first chapter a brief outline of what has happened to the airplane that evolved from the Wrights' flying machine, under the stimulus of practically unlimited funds in two wars, the devotion of the best scientific brains of the age, and the enthusiasm of the public at large. The airplane has come far and fast from its modest prototype, a frail thing of wood, wire, and fabric barely able in calm air to carry two men forty miles in an hour.

Aeronautics very quickly emerged from its pioneering stage of invention and risky experimenting into a prolonged period of intensive government-supported research and development, making use of every aspect of applied science and technology. Metallurgists gave it light alloys and alloy steels; chemists improved its gasoline rations with high-octane vitamins; civil engineers devised new types of strong, light structures; mechanical engineers provided compact engines of ever-increasing output and efficiency; electrical engineers brought radio and radar to aid its navigation; physicists created a new science of aerodynamics with which to refine its external form; and a new kind of professional man, the aeronautical engineer, was added to those who minister to the material needs of society. This engineer designs and builds airplanes to be useful servants in war or peace, plans and operates air transportation systems to serve the public and in general, in his professional efforts, focuses on the airplane the results of the advancing technology of his time.

Public support of aeronautics necessarily involves control and regulation in the public interest. This means control of military development by the Armed Services and control of civil flying by some agency of the state. It would be intolerable anarchy to turn loose in the air above our heads any and all who wish to risk their own necks or to sell tickets to give passengers the same opportunity. Nor can we permit unregulated use of the airspace by foreign flyers, civil or military. For such reasons every country asserts full sovereignty of the airspace above it and attempts to control its use. International treaties define mutual air navigation rights, and under the United Nations there is an International Civil Aeronautics Organization (ICAO), seated at Montreal, to promote uniform operating and safety practices in air commerce.

Civil air transportation began in this country in 1926

with postal contracts to pioneer air lines. An occasional mail contractor would accept a venturesome passenger for a price and stow him among the mailbags. In five years' time it was proved that people would spend money to ride the airways and to send urgent packages, but it was not proved that a passenger and express business could be self-supporting without generous air mail payments from the government. The air mail payment became, in fact, a subsidy authorized by Congress to encourage the development of civil aeronautics. Whether it was a subsidy to the operator, to the users of the air mail service, or to the passenger is immaterial. The effect was to promote a rapid growth, sometimes too rapid, of air transportation.

In 1934 the air lines carried some 500,000 passengers but were losing money. There was cutthroat competition in bidding for air mail contracts and for passengers. There was no control over routes and the principal ones were paralleled by rival lines. Government authority was scattered among many agencies. The investing public had no confidence in air line securities. The record showed that losses in this new business were chronic; it was a leaky bucket for investors' funds. It was testified in 1934 that half of the $120 million invested in air lines had been lost in spite of subsidies.

Although the air lines were improving in safety and reliability as a result of marked technical improvements, they suffered from severe growing pains in the early 1930's, accentuated by the great depression. And the new administration in Washington chose this critical time to shock the sick industry by abrupt cancelation of all air mail contracts, pending extensive investigations and a new deal all round. The ill-fated attempt of the Army Air Corps to fly the mail in the winter of 1934 was a warning before subsequent congressional efforts to legislate the industry into some decent order.

The Civil Aeronautics Act of 1938, which evolved after prolonged discussion, furnished a practical means of reviving and encouraging the air lines. It is a social document of some significance which states continuing social objectives and establishes means to implement its purposes. It marked a peak of cooperation between government and business, for it gave private industry the opportunity to run its own affairs under accountability to a Board with wide powers that acts as umpire.

The act authorized financial aid, when in the public interest, to private air lines that met safety and economic standards but still could not make ends meet. The Civil Aeronautics Board might set rates of mail payment according to need. Mail payments constitute the lever for developing our private air transport system to be adequate for the postal service, the air commerce of the nation, and the national defense. There is currently a move to change the subsidy formula in order to separate out reasonable compensation for carrying the mail from a true subsidy to promote the growth of a particular air line. The touchy subject of a subsidy enters when the public interest requires replacement of once-satisfactory flight equipment by new and better types, or decrees more costly operating practices in the interest of safety, or demands consolidation of air lines or the maintenance of unprofitable routes.

In general, one cannot legislate adequacy. But in this country we have been fortunate to have a strong tide of technical progress. It is implied by the Civil Aeronautics Act to be the duty of the Civil Aeronautics Board to encourage the prompt application of technical improvements in civil aeronautics. The board must match technical possibilities with economic and political realities.

What is the situation now? Can the industry stand on its own feet economically? Is the safety record holding up with higher speeds, flight in worse weather, and congested airports? Can radar and electronics help? Is aeronautics changing city and regional patterns, and are there social effects to be encouraged or to be minimized? These are questions the Civil Aeronautics Board must often consider in making its specific decisions.

In scanning them here, let us first look at the business record.

AIR TRANSPORTATION BUSINESS

Air transport is already "big business," which employed 1,215 airplanes and nearly 80,000 people in 1950. In that year passenger revenue for the domestic air lines exceeded by one-third the total for Pullman travel, the railroad's first-class service. In 1951 the lead was greater. However, Pullman traffic remains about the same, and one must conclude that air transport largely represents the tapping of a new field.

In the first quarter of 1951 the scheduled air lines carried only one-tenth the number of passengers that were carried by the railways, yet the passenger revenues they collected amounted to 66.5% of the railways'. This relatively larger revenue is accounted for by the difference in rates. (The railway figure excludes commuting passengers; the air line figure excludes the operations of the nonscheduled air coach operators.)

The operating revenues of the domestic trunk air lines

for 1951 included some 6% for carrying the mails. The corresponding mail pay given to our overseas air lines was 22% of their total operating revenues. The total air mail payments to both classes of carrier amounted to about $99 million, against which the Post Office recovered some $74 million from air mail postage. The apparent deficit of $25 million was increased to $35 million because of Post Office general expenses allocated to handling and delivering air mail. This postal deficit is said to be somewhat less than the annual deficit incurred on one-cent postcards.

It is evident that many of the domestic air lines are approaching a point where the air mail payment can be strictly for services rendered and without real subsidy. In fact, the four great trunk air lines have already reached this position of self-sufficiency and all subsidy has been eliminated from their mail pay.

United States air transportation in 1951 became a billion dollar industry, with total revenues of $1,043 million. Some 22,900,000 passengers were carried on domestic lines and 2,037,000 on the international lines, marking a gain over 1950 of 32% and 22% respectively.

As growth in earning power is usually a prime determinant in establishing market values of common stocks, it is not surprising that quotations exceed book values as indicated by the following table.[1]

Company	Book Value of Shares	Market Price of Shares	Ratio
American	$34,587,000	$100,019,000	2.89
United	46,130,000	62,086,000	1.35
TWA	30,066,000	50,918,000	1.69
Eastern	36,389,000	59,889,000	1.65

[1] *Aviation Week*, Dec. 17, 1951.

41

American commands the biggest premium, presumably because of the leverage present in the capital structure, with $70 million in senior securities taking precedence over the common stock.

The present relationship of quotations to book values is a significant indication of confidence. Investors and speculators have a very different opinion of the common stock of the New York Central Railroad, for example. This is a high-leverage stock with a last reported book value of $872 million, or nearly eight times its recent market quotation of only $110 million.

Our overseas air lines took in $284 million gross in 1951. The amount of subsidy hidden in their pay for carrying the mail is a measure of the national importance ascribed to means to bring any place in the world only a few hours away from us. In 1950, 54% of all overseas travel in and out of the United States was by air, and 76% of all travel between the United States and outlying possessions.

In 1951 Paris became France's busiest port of entry although a hundred miles from the sea. The capital's two airports saw 74,551 planes land and take off, carrying 1,219,553 passengers, 26,000 tons of air freight, and more than 6,000 tons of air mail.

On May 1, 1952, the eleven transatlantic air lines of the International Air Transport Association are inaugurating an ocean tourist service at reduced rates. Sir William Hildreth, Director General of IATA, calls this "the most daring step since Atlantic air service began."

For years all carriers have agreed that tourist service is good in principle. Tourist fare is sure to attract more passengers, but the question is whether the operators can stand the cost of flying additional passengers. Costs have increased 20% during the past year alone. Most operators will need extra planes to take care of any substantial addition to their passenger traffic, and must place orders for them at today's high prices.

The effect on north Atlantic travel may be felt by the steamship companies even more than by the air lines, though there is still a gap between tourist-class air and sea fares. The first-class one-way steamship fare, in season, New York to England, ranges from $325 to $375, with tourist fares $165-$170. The present first-class one-way fare by air is $395 and the new tourist fare $270, exclusive of the 15 per cent federal transportation tax. The air lines should however tap an untouched market among passengers with a two- or three-week vacation who would not find a trip to Europe possible by ship.

When coast-to-coast flying was first offered, the time was about thirty-two hours compared with less than twelve hours now. Then the fare was $400, now it is $158. Coach fare is $99 without tax. This indicates an aspect of the public's gain in one generation from the air mail deficit.

The Civil Aeronautics Board has in effect urged the air lines to run coach service anywhere at any time, instead of only over selected routes at off-hours. This is bound to have effects on public travel habits, railway and airplane manufacturers, airports and, of course, on the air lines themselves.

The air lines must face four short-term effects of the coach boom: 1) more passengers than they can handle; 2) increased costs with more coach and fewer first-class passengers; 3) overexpansion if traffic does not keep pace with added seating capacity; 4) heavy new financing for additional planes.

The long-term effects may be forecast from what has happened to passenger travel between San Francisco and Los Angeles. In 1948, before air coach came on the route, air travel was 28% of total rail, bus, and air travel. In 1949, the first full year of regular coach service, air's share of the total was 43%. It is expected that it will be more than 50% of all travel in 1951. This means a cut in bus and rail coach business, as well as in first-class rail.

The table below[2] summarizes the relative fares on domestic United States routes for rail and air passengers:

AIR FARES VS. RAIL FARES[2]

	Railroads First-Class	Scheduled Airlines Regular Service	Air Coach
1945	2.95 ¢/mi.	4.95 ¢/mi.	
1946	3.06	4.63	
1947	3.53	5.07	
1948	3.91	5.74	
1949	4.06	5.82	3.96 ¢/mi.
1950	4.17	5.76	4.10
1951	4.23[1]	5.78[2]	4.38[2]
1952	4.25[3]	5.78[4]	3.90[4]

[1] Figures for first eight months of year; include Interstate Commerce Commission-estimated 1-cent Pullman charge plus 3.23-cent basic fare. Rate for 1950 was .92-cent Pullman plus 3.25-cent basic fare.

[2] Figures for first six months of year.

[3] Estimate; assumes no 1952 fare increases. It is based on unofficial Association of American Railroads estimate of fare for last four months of 1951.

[4] Estimated unofficially by CAB Rates division and Air Transport Assn.

SOURCES: Civil Aeronautics Board, Interstate Commerce Commission, Association of American Railroads.

[2] *Aviation Week,* Dec. 31, 1951.

44

Some eighteen local service air lines came into existence after World War II and are making a vigorous growth. They had total revenues of $35 million in 1951, of which half was mail pay. Holding temporary franchises, such carriers are still in the experimental stage from the viewpoint of national policy and are roughly as dependent on mail revenue as were the trunk lines in the early 1930's.

Most of the scheduled air lines carry freight, but their freight revenues in 1951 amounted to only 3% of their combined gross of $1 billion. However, there are a number of new carriers which, by the terms of their certificates, handle nothing but freight. These carriers accounted for about half of all air freight and are making valiant efforts to develop an economically sound business. Freight, as such, seems bound to become a revenue factor of growing importance in the next decade.

It was possible to improvise a miracle of military transport in the summer of 1950. American aviation flew a great tonnage of critically needed troops, arms, ammunition, and supplies across the Pacific Ocean to help hold the Pusan perimeter in Korea. A large portion of the airplanes used for that emergency were chartered from the private air lines, complete with flight crews and ground personnel. Earlier, the Berlin airlift showed what could be done with modern air transport in a different emergency across another ocean.

Just as the merchant marine in wartime is diverted from its lawful occasions in support of sea power, civil air transport can be mobilized in support of air power.

The air line safety record looks pretty good. In 1930 there were 28 fatalities for every 100 million passenger-miles flown by United States domestic air lines. By 1950 this rate had been chopped to 1.2; it rose to 1.4 in 1951, and seems to stabilize around these figures. The risk is evidently satisfactory to the insurance companies who offer passengers a $5,000 policy for 25 cents. The accident rate of our overseas air lines was 2.1 in 1950 and 1.2 in 1951. The nonscheduled air lines flew an estimated one billion passenger-miles in 1951 with a fatality rate of 7.4. The rate for private flying is probably rather bad but firm statistics are not available. The corresponding passenger fatality rate for the railroads was .09, for busses .20, and for automobiles and taxicabs 2.0.

There were five crashes in 1950 on our domestic air lines which were making five million take-offs and landings. This is one accident for a flight mileage equivalent to 32,000 safe trips between New York and Los Angeles. One concludes that scheduled flying is reasonably safe. Nevertheless, it should be made safer. Statistical safety is small comfort to the individual. He cannot know whether or not his number will be called up on his next flight, yet he will be seriously put out if his flight is canceled, postponed, or diverted in the interest of his personal safety.

To some degree, safety and maintenance of schedules are opposed. To improve schedule keeping, flights are made in worse weather, though flights in really bad weather continue to be held up. Faster airplanes will require more elaborate ground facilities and more precise traffic control and aids to navigation if the safety record is to be maintained or improved. Slower airplanes are inherently safer, but progress would be halted by a safety-first policy. Faster airplanes must also fly higher, and again safety can be compromised if the maintenance of pressure in cabins is not foolproof.

In 1950 the domestic air lines completed 98% of the mileage scheduled. Cancelations or delays were due mainly to weather beyond safe standards of operation or to traffic congestion at airports, when the capacity for traffic control was less than the demand for time in the system.

Of all the aids to safe operations under severe weather conditions, the instrument landing system (ILS) probably has contributed the most. It is estimated that in 1950 55% of formerly required cancelations due to weather were eliminated and some 12,000 flights and 500,000 passengers were guided to a safe landing.

Progress has also been made in the technique of air traffic control. In 1947 the capacity of a normal airport permitted seven aircraft to land and seven to depart in an hour when visibility was low. Today, under the same conditions, the potential capacity has been increased to thirty-two arrivals and departures. However, this is not enough, and means must be found to handle greater traffic density with safety.

At present our airways are provided with radio beacons which continuously transmit a direction signal. A pilot can tell from the coded signal he hears whether he is on the airway. The radio-beacon signal is not static free and when most needed it may be unreliable. A tired pilot can misread the signals and follow the wrong range.

The application of modern ultra-high frequency electronics has developed static-free distance-measuring equipment which combined with an omni-range signal, indicates to a pilot his bearing and distance from the ground transmitter, and hence locates his aircraft at all times, either on or off the airway. Such apparatus is now beginning to be installed.

The static-free radio-telephone also uses very high frequency for traffic control. This, in conjunction with surveillance radar, enables the control tower at the airport to direct the landing of numbers of approaching aircraft in orderly sequence.

These new and more trustworthy devices should help to smooth out bad-weather congestion at busy airports, but they are not yet generally available. In the meantime very fast jet-propelled transports are projected which promise to complicate the situation. These high-flying craft cannot be held stacked up over an airport waiting their turn to land. Some system of dispatching must coordinate departure and arrival times to give a clear right of way.

THE HUMAN FACTOR

It has been stated that more than half of all airplane accidents are associated with take-off and landing operations. This may mean that these operations are too difficult or that our airports need improvement. The answer of course is yes on both counts.

One ought to marvel that a normal young man can be hired to launch a fifty-ton machine into the air as a routine task, speed it up to 300 mph, find the specified destination, and then bring it down gently to rest. The young man is no genius but he knows what to do to control the complex apparatus that has evolved from the work of the inventors and engineers of the last half century. He is himself a vital factor in the safety of flying. Medical and physiological science have been intensively applied to methods of selection and training of pilots and to keeping them fit, because there must inevitably be reliance on human judgment, memory, skill, and reactions. These qualities vary not only between individuals but from day to day with the same man.[3]

Recently published statistics give the impression that a high percentage of aircraft accidents have been primarily due to human error, and convey an unpalatable implication that although great strides have apparently been made in increasing the reliability of the airplane very little has been accomplished in reducing the element of human error.[4] Since it is unlikely to be reduced by improving the human being, efforts to cut down accidents by selection and training alone cannot produce a radical improvement. A large proportion of the accidents in recent years could have been prevented by better flying qualities of the airplane, more reliable engines, better weather forecasting, better lighted runways, or some other improvement in whatever it was that made flight conditions so difficult that the pilot made a mistake. As a task increases in difficulty errors grow more frequent. It would seem therefore that errors may be reduced in number and gravity by reducing the difficulty encountered by the human in the performance of his task.

[3] S. S. Stevens, "Aviation Psychology," *Bulletin of the National Research Council, 1,* No. 5.

[4] Group Captain J. A. Newton, "The Human Factor in Aircraft Accidents," *The Journal of the Royal Aeronautical Society, 55,* Feb. 1951.

Progress in airplane design leads to operations that are faster, higher, and in worse weather, and complicated by multiple power plants, pressurization, and radio navigation. Unless the equipment and devices needed for the new features are completely and reliably automatic they expand the field of fallibility.

AUTOMATIC CONTROL

The process of assisting the human pilot by an automatic control system started about 1915 when Lawrence Sperry first demonstrated his gyroscopic pilot. It continues and has reached the stage where autopilots are standard equipment on practically all large airplanes, civil or military. The autopilot replaces the human pilot for routine steering on course and for maintaining the attitude of the airplane against interference from gusts, changes in load distribution and so forth. It is not ordinarily trusted to control take-off and landing operations; in these the human pilot exercises his own judgment and skill. En route he monitors the auto-pilot and can cut it out if it is not working properly.

In general there are three functions in flying that require human skill and judgment. These may be combined in the pilot, or he may be assisted by a flight engineer and a navigator. The pilot's primary job is flying the plane; and in the early days he depended for this on his unaided senses and muscles. In clear weather, with visual information as to attitude and with simple instruments to tell him his course and speed, he is able to do an acceptable job with slow-speed airplanes in sight of the ground (contact flying). When visibility is poor he needs, in addition, gyroscopic instruments to show the orientation and turning rate of his

50

plane in space, and radio aids to indicate his flight path (navigation). Above the clouds he may use celestial navigation if he has a pendulum device to indicate the direction of gravity, a chronometer for accurate time, and an optical device (sextant) to observe the heavenly bodies.

On a long flight a single pilot has much to do, and it is usual to have a flight engineer to monitor the functioning of the engines, propellers, fuel and oil supply, supercharging, and so on, to control what might be called the flight condition and to insure that all is running in optimum adjustment and safety. A navigator is also needed on a long flight to control the flight path. He gets information from dead reckoning, radio and celestial navigation, airway lights and radio beacons, weather reports, airport traffic control towers, and so forth.

A further step in relieving the pilot has been made by the autopilot, which substitutes for his senses three "pick-offs" connected with a gyroscopic mechanism that generates input signals to servos which move the airplane's three sets of controls accordingly. These servos are substituted for the pilot's muscles. His senses are removed as a "feed back" in the "control loop," to use the jargon of the robot designers.

A more recent development combines the autopilot with radio reception devices so that an airplane can be automatically guided along a proper approach path to the airport runway in accordance with radio signals from the airport. Of course the pilot monitors this procedure and can take charge himself by disconnecting the automatic equipment.

A final step to complete automatic control is essential to the guided missile or pilotless aircraft. This takes off, flies a desired course over the earth, and finds or collides with its target without human escort.

The elimination of the pilot means a sophisticated autopilot; elimination of the flight engineer requires automatic adjustment of power and fuel; and elimination of the navigator requires gyroscopic and pendulous references that hold for the time interval of flight, together with an automatic calculator of a high order of versatility. Such a completely automatic system, applied to an airplane, would relieve the pilot of the fatigue of constant attention to attitude, flight condition, and navigation, leaving him free to monitor the operation of the automatic equipment and to exercise his judgment as special situations require. It does

Instrument landing system. Transmitters at the airport maintain a radio beam marking the correct glide path. Radio receivers on the airplane move the two crossed pointers of an instrument to indicate to the pilot the position of his airplane relative to the axis of the radio beam.

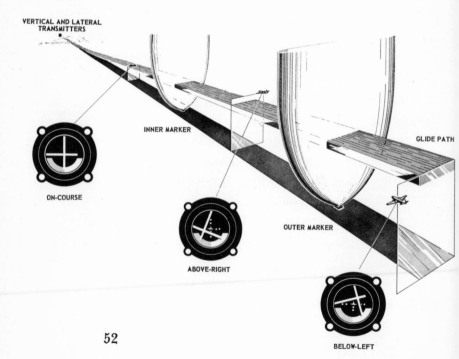

VERTICAL AND LATERAL TRANSMITTERS

INNER MARKER

GLIDE PATH

ON-COURSE

OUTER MARKER

ABOVE-RIGHT

BELOW-LEFT

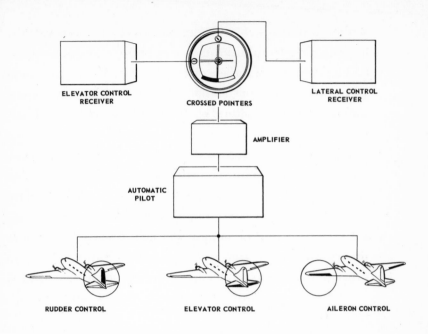

Instrument landing system combined with an autopilot which operates the airplane controls (up-down, right-left) in accordance with amplified electrical signals from two radio receivers. The displacement of the crossed pointers monitors the position of the airplane.

not seem likely that any thinking machine suitable for aircraft use can be expected to compete with a human being in judgment.

The improvement of the safety record for air transportation under the play of conflicting factors is somewhat like the continuing problem of automobile accidents. When the Automobile Safety Foundation was started by Alfred P. Sloan some thirty years ago, the annual automobile death rate was nearly 16 per 100 million vehicle-miles. In 1951 this figure had dropped to 7.1.[5] This improvement has been

[5.] Corresponding to 2.0 on a passenger-miles basis.

achieved in spite of all the factors that increased the hazard, for example more power and speed, more night driving, and more traffic congestion. Better cars, tires, and lights, and better roads and traffic control have overcome the unfavorable factors of technological change in the vehicle.

While the safety record of our domestic air lines is now good, it can be kept so or bettered only by great vigilance and effort as the new high-performance airplanes replace the current types. Safety requires that innovations not be introduced before all supporting facilities are thoroughly proved and ready, and all doubt removed as to the reliability of the new equipment. And there must be emphasis on corresponding improvements in airways, airports, and traffic control.

AIRPORTS

The airport designer is in a dilemma. Airplane and airport and intercommunications must be continually adjusted to accomplish the one critical function for which they exist, in a field that is notorious for rapid and radical change. The designer's great plan may cost $50 million and be financed by a long-term bond issue. He may well fear obsolescence from technical changes in the airplane. Will the runways have to be lengthened or will the location of the airport itself prove to be a mistake?

The few really revolutionary changes in airplane design are conspicuous. The first big break with orderly progress from the days of the Wright brothers came with the Douglas DC-1 in the early 1930's, with the combination of highly loaded metal cantilever wings, landing flaps, high-octane gasoline, and variable-pitch propeller. At once pay-loads and commercial returns were doubled. The new transports required longer runways. Many airports had to be extended. Then came giant four-engined transports, and runways again needed extension and also strengthening. Since the war radio and electronic aids for so-called "blind landings" in fog and rain have determined optimum approach directions which are not always in the direction of existing runways.

The airport designer must now plan for future jet-propelled transports as a carry-over from the current military development of jet bombers. How then, in the face of the certainty of change in the airplane shall he plan ground facilities for the future? And how long is this future? Is the airport investment to justify itself in fifteen years, or must it be frozen for thirty years, the period taken in the monumental air-traffic survey of the Port of New York Authority?

This survey is an appraisal of the effects of all factors, including potential competition from surface transport. It forecasts the volume of things to come by 1980. The reservation is made that the transport airplane is not superseded by some unforeseeable type of flying machine—space ship or atomic-powered rocket. Furthermore, hopefully reasonable assumptions are made that our national economy will continue and expand under private enterprise, and that the dominant role of the United States in world affairs will accelerate foreign trade and travel. The forecast concludes that in thirty years New York should prepare for three times as many air passengers, seven times as much air cargo, six times as much air mail.

A shorter-range view can be based on announced plans

Douglas DC-1 of 1933 which made air transportation commercially feasible

Lockheed Constellation of 1950 used on domestic and international air lines

Vickers Viscount with four turbine-driven propellers. British air transport services inaugurated in 1950

De Havilland Comet. World's first jet airliner. Scheduled services to be inaugurated in 1952 between London and Johannesburg

Washington National Airport, 1951

of the government-operated British Overseas Airways[6] for a jet-propelled round-the-world air service within the next five years. Operations would begin from London to Cairo in 1952, extending later to South Africa and to Singapore. The four-jet Comets now under test are expected to carry up to forty-eight passengers at 500 mph at 40,000 feet. Realization of such travel speed could cut the present round-the-world schedule from eight days to three.

Examination of the characteristics of the Comet and of similar American projects indicates that the runway lengths of fifty American airports (5,780 feet average) are adequate.[7] These airports handle 84% of domestic air traffic. The fortunate thing here is that the thin air at the high altitudes where the high-speed jet planes must fly for the sake of economy requires relatively large wings. This makes landing easier. With the large thrust from the jets, such airplanes will accelerate rapidly to flying speed in a reasonable distance.

There will be trouble with the length of run required for landing jet transports, if they are more heavily loaded, until more effective braking methods are developed for them. It is still true that 10,000-foot runways, such as heavy bombers need, would allow the airplane designer further to improve jet plane performance.

Can future airplanes be designed to conform to airport limitations and still take full advantage of improvements made possible by technical progress? Research airplanes

[6.] *New York Times*, Aug. 7, 1951.

[7.] W. T. Dickenson, "Airport Requirements for Future Transport Aircraft", *National Air Review*, Washington, D. C., April 1951, pp. 11, 15.

have recently flown at supersonic speeds at high altitude. They could not have operated from existing airports. It may be many years before the results of such research are applied in air transportation, but at some unpredictable time clever designers backed by bold promoters will do it. Probably they will demand a special airport for a special service.

I venture to suggest a parallel with the much older problem of the naval architect. He designs ships which must enter certain harbors and pass through certain canals. Tankers for Persian Gulf oil conform to Suez Canal restrictions on draft. United States naval vessels must be able to pass through the locks of the Panama Canal. As the art of shipbuilding progressed larger vessels became practicable and were proposed by builders and operators. Pressure on port authorities resulted in deeper channels and longer piers. Eventually larger vessels were built. The great Atlantic liners can enter only a few large ports. World-ranging tramp steamers are designed to enter almost any port. Under the combined influence of geographic and economic considerations and technical possibilities, a merchant marine has evolved consisting of various kinds and sizes of vessels, with corresponding port facilities.

I think it is probable that air transportation, influenced by analogous factors, will develop in a similar way, with airplanes designed for the specific airports served and airports designed to accommodate the kind of air transportation the community desires and can afford. It may prove both unsafe and impractical to handle all types of transport planes at the same airport. A great city may well have several airports, each organized to handle one class of traffic. Congress has authorized a second airport for Washington some fifteen miles away in Virginia; the present airport might be relegated to serving local and unscheduled air traffic. There is already a tendency to remove flying schools and private flyers from main airports.

The evolution of ground facilities will now lead, now lag behind the requirements of the airplane designer. Change in the basic scheme will come about in response to pressures, not continuously but at infrequent intervals, just as vessels and their port facilities have been adjusted to each other over the last century.

PRIVATE FLYING

Doing something "just for the fun of it" has become the supreme form of luxury, and in the intensely militarized world of aviation those who fly for pleasure are now few indeed. At one time governments could be persuaded to assist flying clubs and civil air patrols in return for the benefits of a reserve of trained pilots, but mass training schemes are now the rule. Practically all flying that is not military is now concerned with a business or vocation. In the United States, private flying is geographically favored, but the sale of personal airplanes since 1946 has fallen nearly 50% each year. And in Europe the chill change in the postwar political and economic climate has withered any hope for pleasure flying.

It has been said that there has been a failure to develop a foolproof light airplane offering reasonable utility to its owners. This may be true, but the fact remains that the cost of owning and flying an airplane has risen by at least 400% since 1946. The young people who were expected to take to flying by the thousands in the air age simply can-

Experimental light plane of Professor O. C. Koppen of M.I.T. Leading edge slats, trailing edge flaps, and large propeller allow low-speed landing and take-off on a 100-yard strip of grass.

not afford to spend so large a proportion of their monthly earnings in this way.

An official government survey made in 1946 predicted that one million personal airplanes would be in operation in this country by 1955. Of the 90,000 such planes now registered, half are flown less than sixty hours a year; they are not really useful to their owners. The official forecast failed to allow for the inherent shortcomings of the light airplanes available and for the costs of ownership.

There seems to be no immediate prospect of radical change in the situation while we are so intensely preoccupied with the threat of war. However, in the long run we may expect private enterprise, in a more favorable climate, to apply the results of available research to the light airplane, to its very great improvement in safety and utility. Unpredictable inventions will be made and costs will come down as manufacturing volume is achieved. A light airplane should not cost more than an automobile except for this matter of volume.

Whether the helicopter will provide the aerial vehicle for the individual who wishes to go places quickly is not yet clear, but its advantage of starting from his backyard rather than from a distant airport is impressive. It has already proved itself versatile and economical, adapting to crop spraying, visiting inaccessible regions, or wherever its unique ability is required. It is possible with helicopters to

Igor Sikorsky in his helicopter, Stratford, Conn., May 1940

shift groups of men from one part of a battlefield to another, by-passing roadblocks or other obstacles. In Korea it has been invaluable for quick communications between front lines and headquarters, for evacuation of wounded, delivery of special supplies or personnel, and in general to oversee the whole operation. This has, of course, been possible because of the absence of serious air opposition. That the tactical value of helicopters is appreciated is evidenced by a hundredfold increase in orders to the industry in 1951.

The atomic bomb and the snorkel-equipped submarine may render future large-scale landings on a hostile beach impractical by interdicting any great concentration of vessels just off shore. It is suggested that assault troops could take off in helicopters from dispersed vessels at sea, land in the rear of the beach defenders and seize a beachhead for the first wave of assault boats bearing the heavy equipment. Here the helicopter does not replace troop-carrying airplanes which can drop a whole airborne division. Its role is rather in moving a limited number of men for a tactical purpose. This has been demonstrated by the United States Marines with their assault-transport helicopters.

For commercial utility future helicopters should be built larger. A committee of experts appointed to advise the British Minister of Civil Aviation reported that to be economically self-sustaining helicopters should carry at least twenty passengers, have two engines and be able to fly on one only, and have a range of 300 miles. The committee expected that such craft could be developed and made available by 1958.

Since the helicopter is now being intensively developed because of its military advantages, we may feel hopeful that most of its handicaps will soon be removed. Compared

64

Piasecki transport helicopter, 1951

with an airplane, the present helicopter is costly and relatively inefficient as a load carrier. It is slow, has a short range, vibrates badly under some conditions, and has difficult handling characteristics which prevent blind flying.

These handicaps are not fundamental. Future designs should eliminate the articulated rotor with its vibration and limitation on forward speed by blade stalling. An autopilot has recently been demonstrated to provide good stability and control for a standard helicopter. The future helicopter could have a payload equal to that of an airplane

65

designed for the same speed, and still have the ability to hover. It is fairly safe to predict that before long we shall see helicopters shuttling between airports and downtown roof-top terminals with "bus loads" of passengers.

THE SEAPLANE

The seaplane, either a true flying boat with wings or an airplane with floats, appeared in the early days of aviation. In this country development began with the pioneer inventions of Glenn Curtiss of Hammondsport, New York, and was carried forward by the Navy's interest. The Navy wanted aircraft with the fleet for scouting and control of gunfire; it provided a launching catapult aboard ship to push off a small seaplane, and a boat crane to hoist it aboard again after it had landed in the water alongside. This arrangement was severely limited in utility by weather, and was eventually scrapped in favor of a special flush-deck vessel, the carrier, to furnish a seagoing base for a large number of airplanes. Small seaplanes were thereafter abandoned although they then held the world's speed records.

The Navy had a second use for aircraft: scouting and submarine hunting. For this mission large flying boats based on sheltered harbors proved effective. The flying boats had to be big in order to carry large bombs and fuel loads for long flights. Endurance was the first requirement. Submarine warfare gave an enormous incentive for the development of bigger flying boats. This development culminated in the Navy-Curtiss flying boat NC-4 which made the first crossing of the Atlantic by air in May, 1919.

Civil air lines operating overseas at first adopted flying

66

boats but changed to airplanes as large airports with concrete runways became available. The flying boats proved expensive to maintain. The U. S. Navy, however, kept its patrol boats through the 1930's and used them to spearhead the step-by-step island campaign in the South Pacific.

The present technical situation seems to be that large flying boats are competitive with large airplanes in speed and efficiency and may have an advantage in the very largest sizes. However, they are restricted to ice-free shel-

Naval F5L flying boat, 1918

Navy-Curtiss flying boat, NC-4, leaving Trepassy Bay
on first trans-Atlantic flight, May 1919

tered water for landing and in general are more difficult
to load and service. It is true that the most economical
aircraft for any given route is the largest aircraft which the
traffic potential will fill. This seems to point toward a giant
flying boat, but geography determines the decision. A large
expanse of sheltered water free from shipping and other
hazards to landing is unlikely to be near the city that orig-
inates the traffic. Remote tropical lagoons do not generate
heavy commercial traffic.

The development of lighter-than-air vehicles or airships has had a history somewhat similar to that of the seaplane. Although the airship preceded the airplane, it began its practical development with the advent of the light internal combustion engine.

At first called dirigible balloons, early airships consisted of a streamlined gas bag supporting a car. They were fair-weather craft, but had the great virtue of remaining aloft when the engine failed. Their development centered in Europe and they had some application in the first World War for submarine hunting.

In the early 1900's Germany supported the radical ideas of Count Zeppelin and constructed a series of large airships. The Zeppelin airship had a rigid framework enclosing a number of gas cells and carrying several engines. It was relatively immune from failure of a gas cell or an engine, but its hydrogen constituted a fire hazard and its great size made it unmanageable in a storm.

The Zeppelins, in the early part of the first World War, perpetrated the first bombings of a civil population, but such raids over London and Paris were soon abandoned. The incendiary bullets of fighter airplanes forced the Zeppelins to restrict subsequent operations to reconnaisance at sea.

The discovery of noninflammable helium gas in the United States promised to render the Zeppelin-type airship less vulnerable, and the U. S. Navy after the war undertook to carry on its development here. One Zeppelin, later named the "Los Angeles," was acquired from Germany, and three —the "Shenandoah," "Akron," and "Macon"—were built here. The Navy experimented with these airships as scouts in war games, and similar airships were projected for air transport operations. However, after weather and other operating hazards had proved disastrous, the naval rigid-airship program was abandoned.

About the same time it became clear that experiments with heavier-than-air craft had progressed so far that the airship's great endurance, its chief virtue, could be had with multi-engined planes, and transatlantic flight in all weathers would soon be possible.

The postwar German exploits of Dr. Hugo Eckener with the round-the-world flight of his "Graf Zeppelin" kept airship enthusiasm alive for a time, and his transatlantic service begun with the airship "Hindenburg" seemed to point to a commercial future for such vessels. Then came the explosion of the hydrogen-filled "Hindenburg" to close the book on this aspect of aeronautics.

While the rigid airship proved to be a false start, one important technological advance carried over to the airplane. The strong light alloy of copper and aluminum called duralumin which was developed for the Zeppelins became the basic structural material for all airplanes. The fabric-covered wing of the 1920's was replaced by a smooth cantilevered metal wing in the monoplane in the 1930's.

A word is due about the less ambitious nonrigid airships, the blimps. They were found useful for naval patrol work and mine sweeping but had no claim to utility for air transport. The Navy continued their development during the period between wars, and their value increased with the availability of modern acoustic, magnetic, and electronic devices for detecting submarines. In World War II, the Navy had blimps guarding the approaches to our Atlantic and Pacific ports. United States blimps kept watch off Brazil and Venezuela and along the shores of North Africa when our landings took place. Six blimps flew across the Atlantic via the Azores to guard the Strait of Gibraltar. Admiral Rosendahl reported that "after Airship Squadron Fourteen began operations in the Gibraltar area in June 1944, not a single enemy submarine passed through the Strait, either by day or night."[8] The helium-filled airship equipped with a great variety of submarine-detecting devices seems to be an established naval unit.

[8.] *Airship Operations in World War II*, U. S. Naval Air Station, Lakehurst, N. J., April 1946.

Navy blimp over U.S.S. *Threadfish;* maneuvers off Block Island, 1947

Fairchild Packets C-119; logistic support by air freight, 1950

I have tried in this chapter to make an over-all survey of the present state of air transportation, with some speculation as to the effects of continuing technological progress. I think it can be taken as sure that current progress will bring about faster and more economical aircraft with increased use of automatic devices to minimize human error in piloting and navigation. Also, special electronic facilities for safe traffic control at airports should permit a greatly increased volume of air transportation.

The obvious vehicle for efficient air transportation is the airplane, which even after fifty years of intensive development is capable of substantial improvement in performance, economy, and safety. The flying boat and the airship appear to have inherent characteristics which make them useful only for special purposes. However, the helicopter does promise to meet shorthaul and commuter requirements when its peculiar advantages can be exploited. I venture to predict the extensive incorporation of helicopters in the air transport pattern of the future.

As the trend goes now, I cannot find a basis to expect the development of light airplanes flying for fun that was once hoped for. The evolution of flying is not paralleling that of the motorcar, although sportsmen were the first to take up each vehicle. The private automobile preceded the truck and bus. In aeronautics we now have the equivalent of the truck and bus but not swarms of private airplanes. Perhaps it is just as well that our generation suffers from traffic congestion only on the highways.

III. SOCIAL AND POLITICAL EFFECTS

I have spoken of the Civil Aeronautics Act as a social document because it implements a national policy to shape the social impact of a branch of technology. This act governs civil aeronautics and especially air transport. Other United States statutes make the application of aeronautics to national defense the function of the Defense Department, and give the state, as represented by the President, responsibility for aeronautical research.

74

The National Advisory Committee for Aeronautics was established by Congress in 1915 as an independent agency for the "scientific study of the problems of flight with a view to their practical solution." Members of this committee are appointed by the President and serve without compensation. The committee acts like a board of directors in guiding a research staff numbering more than seven thousand. With its three great laboratories in Virginia, Ohio, and California, the NACA constitutes one of the major research organizations of the world. Its research has, for a generation laid the groundwork for aeronautical advance in this country.[1] That its efforts have been effective is perhaps best attested by the acknowledged superiority of the aircraft designed and produced by the American aircraft industry. Our military and naval aircraft have played leading parts in winning wars in Europe, Africa, Asia, and the western Pacific. Our transport planes are the standard equipment of the most of the world's air lines.

NACA research is conducted with public funds, and results are published when in the public interest, or, when restricted for security reasons, are transmitted to the Armed Services and to the industry in the form of confidential reports of engineering data and methods of analysis and prediction.

The act establishing NACA formerly provided, I believe, a unique example of research in a field of applied science undertaken by the state; but the example is no longer

[1.] Vannevar Bush, *Modern Arms and Free Men* (New York, Simon and Schuster, 1949), p. 22.

Launching of research rocket, Corporal E, White Sands Proving Ground, New Mexico, September 1951

unique since Congress more recently charged the Atomic Energy Commission with responsibility for research in another field of applied science. The concern of the state with progress in aeronautics is understandable because of the primary obligation of self-defense. We cannot afford to be second best in the kind of world we now know. Civil Aeronautics, on the other hand, offers not terrors but the hope of a better world order.

EFFECTS OF AIR TRANSPORTATION

In the age of air transport, distances are beginning to be thought of in hours rather than in miles. At the present time we can fly a third of the way round the world, from San Francisco to Paris, in 30 hours. A businessman can go from New York to Chicago by train in 17 hours and the cost is $115 if he counts his travel time as worth $4 an hour. He can go by air in 3 hours 15 minutes which, with salary hours added to the plane fare, makes the air journey cost him less than $60. Similar arithmetic applied to a San Francisco journey works out to nearly $500 by Pullman and about $200 by air, without the Federal transportation tax. The incentive to use the airplane for business is evident.

The Port of New York Authority, which has a good reputation for forecasts of future traffic, estimates that by 1970 air travel will exceed rail travel for distances between 150 and 1,000 miles, and air transport will carry virtually all the common carrier passengers moving more than 1,000 miles. It is also predicted that half of letter mail will move by air.

Let us note as a derivative effect that air transport by its competition has begun to change the railroads. Local passenger trains have been disappearing from the rails because of the competition of the motor-bus and private automobile; air transportation now promises to accelerate their disappearance. Once the subject of innumerable tales of the traveling salesman, the "rattlers" may soon join the horsecars in transportation museums.

Unprofitable local and branch lines account for a substantial part of the railway's chronic loss from passenger transportation. Last year this operating deficit was half a billion dollars. The Atlantic Coast Line is reported to have cut out ten trains and saved $1.5 million in annual operating expense.[2] The Southern Railway saved $1.6 million in the same way. Main line trains are streamlined and faster, cars are cleaner and carry more agreeable attendants—perhaps partly in reflection of the sleek appearance of the airplane and its stewardess.

Concurrent with the growth of air line operations we have recently seen a mushrooming of miscellaneous aviation enterprises: crop dusting, spraying, power- and pipeline patrols, surveys, forest fire fighting, and carrying people and supplies by air on all sorts of urgent missions. A dramatic example was Operation Locust in Iran. A call for help to check a plague of locusts was met by a flight of three transports to Iran, carrying eight small airplanes with spray equipment, nine pilots, six mechanics, and thirteen tons of a special chemical.

Air cargo has quadrupled since 1946 though it does not yet handle heavy goods. It does take almost anything that can be got through a plane's door for which time in transit is valuable: fashion goods, flowers and fruits, drugs and chemicals, films, electrical goods, sea food, light machinery

2. *Wall Street Journal,* Dec. 10, 1951.

and parts, documents, money, and hundreds of other items.

The airplane is changing the distribution methods of merchants and manufacturers, their inventory controls, and even their purchasing habits. For example, the market for perishable fruits shipped from a distance varies widely in different cities according to arrivals. This makes a hardy gambler of the California shipper by rail. He can now ship by cargo plane overnight and sell his produce in top condition for a definite market price. The result is a more stable market and less waste and loss.

"Ghost lands" around airports are coming alive as new factories occupy the vacant areas. As industrial developments have taken place near Los Angeles, San Francisco, Cleveland, Dallas, St. Louis, and Phoenix airports, land values have risen. Small manufacturers, who are in the majority among the newcomers, make many small-volume shipments by air freight and count on two- or three-day delivery. A distributor, for example, orders a $400 chain saw after he has secured a customer. He collects from the buyer in time to take advantage of a 1% discount for ten-day payment. The air freight charge is $8, discount $4, making the net cost of air freight the same as by rail. In addition the distributor has no inventory expense.

The garment industry was one of the earliest to make use of air cargo. A retailer can venture a small order of a new item. If it sells, he can reorder and have it by air next day. He can keep his inventory at a minimum and yet offer greater variety.

The air lines have cooperative arrangements with trucking concerns by which delivery of air cargo can be made at some 500 air line stops and, by truck, to 2,500 off-air line points.

Domestic air parcel post has been inaugurated, making possible overnight delivery. What will be the effect of such time-saving on our great merchandizing institutions? Will the mail order houses make further inroads into local retailing? Will the housewife do more of her shopping by mail?

The railroad delivered mail and newspapers and various urban products to the wagon pioneers. The automobile brought remote villages into the social and economic community dominated by the towns. The radio has gone even further in impressing urban tastes and ideas upon every home. All over the country one town is a lot like another. Hundreds of small towns even look alike. There has been a mingling of people due to ease of transportation and communication. Labor is mobile and becomes migratory in times of economic dislocation. With the national and international mobility afforded by air transport, national frontiers should be less marked by regional prejudices and less of a barrier to mutual understanding.

In this country the automobile has brought to many of us the advantages of suburban life. The worker in a large city who lives near his work is an exception. There is a trend toward a separation between business and domestic life, a trend that may be sharpened as air transport is extended to commuters. Short-haul air transport has yet to be developed, but it conceivably could extend the daily commuting distance well beyond fifty miles. While more than half our population is now urban, the next generation should see this figure reduced. There are already signs of serious decay in the central residence areas of large cities like Boston and Cleveland.

The influence of air transport on business extends beyond

the convenience of buyers and sellers. It facilitates the central management of widely scattered enterprises. Branch factories were helped by the long-distance telephone, then by air mail, and now by air transport of key personnel. The current political pressure for so-called industrial dispersion, to locate new plants away from existing concentrations, originated with plans for civil defense. But there is already a natural trend away from giant industrial centers, which should favor the growth of the smaller towns.

In the Southwest air transport has already substantially expanded trading areas. The new business that has come to Dallas and Fort Worth may be indicative of changing trading habits that tend to concentrate commerce in the cities while industry leaves them. A local service air line with headquarters in Dallas extends to the Gulf Coast at

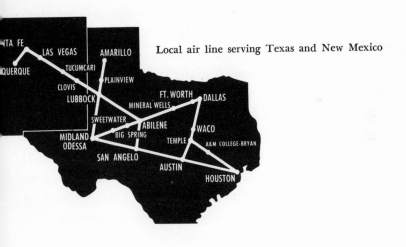

Local air line serving Texas and New Mexico

Houston, to the Texas Panhandle, and along the old Santa Fe Trail into Albuquerque. Another branch ties in the state capital and the west Texas oil fields. This regional carrier, Pioneer Air Lines, serves 22 cities in two states. In 1950 it carried 130,000 passengers, of whom 71% traveled on business, 22% for recreation, and 7% because of an emergency. Of the total number of passengers, 40% made connections with other carriers going outside the region. Such a regional air service operates with an average "hop" of 30 minutes.

The influence of an airport on a city is already something to reckon with. The airport is, for practical technical reasons, outside the city proper. Problems of rail and highway access and traffic flow arise at once. New communities grow up around a busy airport; it is estimated that some 35,000 people will soon have settled around New York's Idlewild Airport. Special kinds of business are attracted, and real estate values change with this spreading out of population and employment.

A busy airport is a source of employment and an economic asset to the neighboring population but, at the same time, it can be a potential hazard and a noisy nuisance. The adjustment of conflicting interests between an airport and an established population becomes highly charged with emotion after such accidents as have recently occurred near the Newark Airport. The problem is especially difficult in the case of the older airports, originally located when air traffic was not intensive and laid out for the operation of relatively small air planes. Relocation at a distant site is a very costly solution.

If, as I believe possible, we see the evolution of a pattern for a metropolitan area with several airports, each designed for a particular class of air traffic, existing airports may be salvaged by rearrangement of their facilities. For example, a downtown airport might handle only short-haul traffic in smaller planes, restricted to parallel runways pointing in a direction to divert traffic away from the city.

Once we allowed steam trains to run along city streets to a downtown terminal. Now we take it for granted that railway traffic must be segregated. Eliminating grade crossings, using electric or diesel locomotives for terminal access, and locating freight yards in industrial areas have largely eliminated conflicts between the railroad and the city.

The location and layout of a new airport presents a fascinating problem to city and regional planners who must consider the convenience of air line patrons and the safety of the departing and arriving aircraft as well as control of land use by zoning regulations to minimize hazard to the settlements that are sure to grow up because of the airport.

A pattern of several special airports for overseas, trunk line, freight, local, and miscellaneous air traffic will require an effective central traffic control of all aircraft flying over the metropolitan area, and the air equivalent of taxi and bus service. I believe that electronic systems are now available to handle air traffic and that helicopters can be developed to transport passengers and mail as required.

The problem of locating a new airport is made more difficult by the need for longer runways for large jet-propelled planes—which will also be more noisy—and made easier by the fact that modern air transports can operate regardless of wind direction except under gale conditions, as was demonstrated both in the Berlin airlift and by our bombers that operated of necessity from single direction runways on Pacific islands. It seems unnecessary, therefore, to provide long runways in several directions. Since many existing airports cannot be extended, there will be pressure to provide new airports for the big planes.

Air transportation, as competitive private enterprise, is developing under the pressure of technological progress, stimulated by the state and yet regulated by the state. There are two groups of planners, the managers of air lines and the Civil Aeronautics Board in Washington. Both realize that the public wants to go faster, that there is a dangerous relation between speed and safety, that the air transport system is vital to national defense, and that economic collapse of this private industry is unthinkable.

The planners are always in difficulties from past mistakes and future uncertainties. No major industry has ever progressed so rapidly as air transport or expanded so fast. It has been the darling of the state and has had unprecedented favors. On the other hand, the industry has not reached maturity and must grow up through a maze of economic and technical difficulties. It must make correct decisions now about things it cannot afford to change later, and about a future only dimly foreseen.

In the past the air lines have made some serious mistakes, for which the government regulators are not entirely free of blame. An example was the gross overestimation of traffic potential at the end of the war and the naïve assumption that high wartime patronage would be a permanent feature of the business. The resultant overexpansion of routes, schedules, and equipment would have wrecked any industry not related closely to the government. Thanks to its sheltered position, the industry has survived and is now soberly considering the probable near-

84

term obsolescence of its present new airplanes and their replacement by faster jet-propelled planes costing much more.

The over-all development cost of a large jet transport would probably exceed $20 million, and the builder would need large orders to recover his costs from a sales price of the order of $2.5 million each. It is probable that a capacity for fifty to seventy passengers and a speed of 600 mph will be required to render such equipment economical. The doubled speed over current transports should permit more frequent trips and almost doubled revenue per month. Assuming a start in 1952, it would take five to seven years to place a new type in service, but the air lines need this period to amortize their present airplanes and those now on order.

The Civil Aeronautics Administration is faced with the prospect of scrapping much of its present—not yet fully installed—airways communications, navigation, and flight-control equipment in favor of the newer ultra-high frequency and microwave apparatus needed now for safety of airway traffic. Furthermore, the Defense Department has embarked on the immense task of providing a radar screen around the continent with a corresponding communications, navigation, and flight-control network for our air defense forces. The military system must be compatible with the civil airways system.

The legal concept of sovereignty above the surface of the earth is much older than human flight. The Romans, for example, kept the airspace above public highways and sacred ground open by law. The foundation of present international air law is the Paris Convention of 1919, part of the Versailles Treaty, which stated that "the High Contracting Parties recognize that every power has complete and exclusive sovereignty over the airspace above its territory." The extent of this airspace was undefined. Subsequently, this same principle of airspace sovereignty was incorporated into the law of the United States in the Air Commerce Act of 1926, which asserted that "the United States has complete sovereignty of the airspace over the lands and waters of the United States including the Canal Zone."

The exercise of sovereignty supposes some practical action for control and enforcement. It is not a purely academic question. It has been held that the territory of a state is limited by the ability of that state to make its law effective. In the 17th century the Dutch jurist Bynkershoek evolved from established practice the now generally accepted principle that "dominion seaward is limited to the extent to which it is possible to enforce it," a principle which created the concept of territorial waters, the three-mile limit (cannon-shot range), and indirectly influenced the suppression of fictitious blockades. This would be a harsh rule to apply to the airspace. Only a few great states have power to control the airspace above their surface ter-

[3.] Based on an address by John C. Cooper at Escuela Libre de Derecho, Mexico City, Jan. 5, 1951.

ritory. Weak states have no such power. The possession of power should not determine international right.

The development of world-wide air transportation creates legal problems without precedent in international law. The ancient principle of unlimited sovereignty is already altering in these times of interdependence, in favor of international agreements and the delegation to the United Nations of powers once reserved to individual states. It seems clear that the concept of freedom of the high seas from the exercise of sovereignty by any state can have no parallel in the ocean of air above the territorial airspace of the states. Freedom of passage over the high seas does not threaten the very existence of a state as does the passage of hostile aircraft directly overhead. High-altitude intercontinental rockets, which might even become earth satellites, passing high above the surface territory of many states could give international lawyers, among others, a very unhappy time. And the airspace above the Arctic is not yet subject to the acknowledged sovereignty of any state, though it is certain that air routes will traverse the top of the world.

The Arctic Airspace

Potential air routes across the Arctic are the shortest distances between important parts of the Northern Hemisphere and are sure to be exploited for air commerce. Yet there is great uncertainty as to the right to fly through the Arctic airspace and to establish landing fields and facilities on the ice. The airspace over the high seas is acknowledged to be free for the use of aircraft of all states. But it will be necessary to decide whether any part of the ice-covered water beyond normal territorial waters may be subject to the sovereignty of a particular state and not treated as part of the high seas.

A difficulty is raised by the so-called "sector" theory under which a state facing the pole is supposed to have rights in the triangle between its recognized territory and the North Pole itself. Canada and Russia have asserted such claims but the sector theory has not been accepted by international agreement and is opposed by the United States.

The Arctic Ocean proper contains no known land. It is almost continuously covered with ice in slow motion. The Russians in 1937-38 made a fruitless effort to place a "permanent" settlement near the North Pole. When their party was rescued, the total drift in 274 days had been approximately 1,500 miles. Obviously a fixed installation is impossible.

Nevertheless such ice-covered seas can be controlled from the air to exercise sovereignty. The same thing might be said of the open seas, but in that case an attempt by a single state in time of peace to seize any part of the high seas and the airspace above it, for purposes of exclusive control, would be an act of aggression against all other states.

John C. Cooper of the Institute for Advanced Study concludes an examination of the problems of the Arctic airspace as follows: "The airspace over the Arctic Ocean is and should be as free for the aircraft of all States, whether having land territories in the Arctic or not, as is the airspace over the other great water areas of the world."[4]

[4.] "Airspace Rights over the Arctic," *Air Affairs,* New York, Dec. 1950, pp. 516, 540.

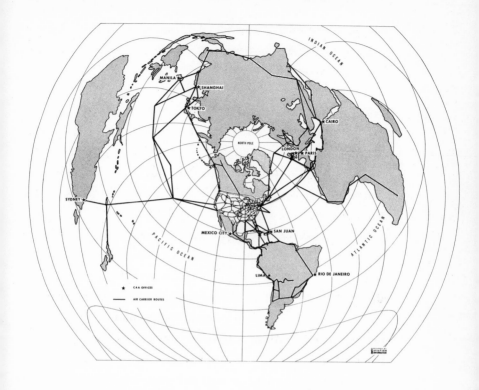

United States air carrier routes

We may reasonably assume that the development of Arctic air routes will proceed as commercial incentives develop and international agreements are consummated to provide the facilities necessary for safe and reliable schedules. Meteorological conditions are favorable, flight distances are well within the capability of modern aircraft, and the techniques of efficient cold-weather operations are at hand.

89

Most of the land of this globe is north of the 35th degree of north latitude. Air routes, military or civilian, tend to converge toward the North Pole. The longer the distance the closer the convergence. In an aeronautical concept of geography, the Arctic is the center of the world. Long-range movements of military aircraft will cross the Arctic area and should be identified or intercepted there.

A Defense Identification Zone has been established around the United States, including Alaska, extending 300 miles beyond the borders. A civil airplane before departure must announce its flight plan and route of entry. On entering this controlled zone, the plane is followed by a radar system. If an unidentified aircraft is spotted, interceptors go out from the nearest base. The installation of a radar screen over the far north is progressing rapidly. Col. Bert Balchen has stated: "I can't see that any aircraft could get into the North American continent unnoticed."[5]

AIR POWER

I have discussed the airplane as a tool which in peace is applied to air transportation to bring us the good things that come from increased mobility. Let us look also at the tool as applied to war. In the hands of an enemy it carries a threat of surprise and overwhelming destruction. The atomic bomb amplifies its destructive potential. The doctrine of retaliation in kind gives small satisfaction if we must imagine a climax of mutual extermination. We seek security in our ability to control the airspace above us and to defend ourselves against an aggressor by early interception of his aircraft.

[5.] *Wings Club Bulletin*, New York, Sept. 1951.

The complex of resources needed to give a nation control of the airspace against a challenge is commonly called air power. The term need not be defined in detail, but it includes as its foundation scientific and industrial resources adequate to produce superior airplanes and weapons, as well as the air forces to use them. Our air forces are at present organized by function in accordance with the current ideas of military planners. These ideas change with technical progress and with the international climate and are now the subject of anxious debate in Congress.

First there is the Strategic Air Command operating the long-range bombers of the U. S. Air Force. Its mission as General LeMay defines it is "to effect the progressive destruction and disintegration of an enemy's war-making capacity to a degree where he no longer retains the means or will to wage war." To continue quoting General LeMay: "Strategic Air Command is trained to destroy a warring nation's economic system by wiping out centers of industry, government, communication, and transport, as well as sources of power and stockpiles of strategic materials. Strategic bombing in war must be a sustained operation . . . for decisive results cannot be accomplished with a single bomb by a single raid."[6]

Reliance on strategic bombing is limited by a natural reluctance to begin it, by the belief of many that indiscriminate area bombings of British and German cities in the first part of the last war strengthened the will to resist, by doubt of moral justification, and by a realization that victory by such means carries responsibility for restoration of

[6.] Lt. Gen. Curtis E. LeMay, "Strategic Air Command," *The Sperryscope*, New York, *12*, No. 6, 1951, 5.

the wrecked nation. Furthermore, great advances have recently been made in the defense against strategic bombing, both by interceptor aircraft and by antiaircraft missiles and guns. Early warning by modern radar methods also makes the element of surprise more difficult to achieve.

Convair B-36D, jet-augmented version of intercontinental strategic bomber with four jet engines supplementing six piston engines

Boeing B-47A swept-wing six-jet bomber

An effective strategic air force requires aircraft of great flight capacity to penetrate unaided into the heart of enemy country. Isolationist thinking tends to emphasize the possibility of destroying an enemy by so-called intercontinental attack. The giant B-36 is stated by General

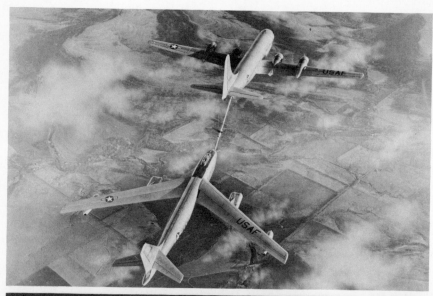

Aerial refueling of Republic F-84 fighter. Refueling time two and one-half minutes

(Left) Aerial refueling of B-47 bomber from tanker airplane by means of flying boom, a telescopic swiveling pipe from tail of tanker to coupling in nose of bomber

Swift fighter with Rolls-Royce Avon jet engine in production for Royal Air Force

LeMay to be "capable of operating from bases in the United States against targets anywhere in the world." However, the fast medium bombers which represent the bulk of the Strategic Air Command's striking force have shorter range and require bases near the enemy. For such forward bases allies are needed and large supporting forces of escort fighters, tanker aircraft, and air transports. The bases, moreover, must be secure against both land and air attack.

The reverse function of the Strategic Air Command is that of the Air Defense Command, whose mission is to defend the country against air attack. Its equipment is designed for interception and air combat. As a force in being, it must have a well-advertised capacity to discourage an enemy's aggression; a weak defense might constitute an invitation.

Then there is the more recently established Tactical Air Command. Its target priorities are, first, the enemy air force (to gain control of the air); second, enemy reinforcements and supply lines (to isolate the battlefield); and last, battlefield targets in close support of our own troops. Marine Corps aviation is an example of a tactical air force attached directly to a ground force for its close support.

There is currently a controversy as to whether a tactical air force should be under the control of the commander of an army, to be used as he directs, or under an air force commander whose operations will be coordinated with those of the army by some higher authority. The argument seems sound that the army commander is responsible for his battle and should control all elements engaged in it. On the other hand, air superiority cannot be risked for urgent close-support strikes called for from foxholes. The present doctrine leaves over-all command with the theater

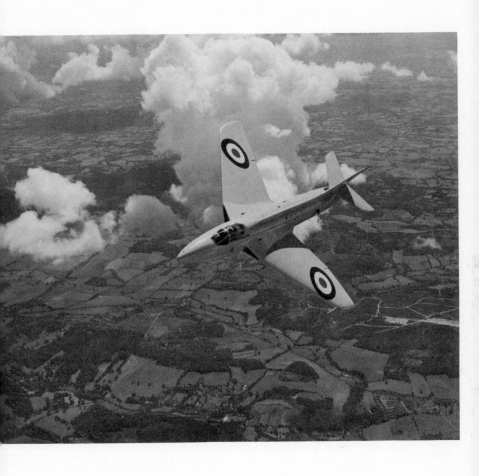

Hawker P-1067 high-speed RAF fighter

commander, as was the case with General MacArthur in the Pacific. This involves a complicated chain of communications to get a call for help answered with effect rather than with a debate at headquarters. The conflict of views really concerns only operational control of those tactical aircraft assigned to close support of ground troops in the front lines. The primary mission of the Air Force, to achieve and maintain air superiority, does not seem to be in dispute.

Some "air age" enthusiasts have visions of a cheap, quick victory by push-button war, and have tried via the press and Congress to scuttle the Navy and Marine Corps and to restrict the Army to mopping-up and occupation functions. Such foolishness seems to erupt whenever new possibilities capture the imagination of undisciplined minds. Kaiser Wilhelm was badly misled into unrestricted submarine warfare. Hitler was carried away by his air enthusiasts into terror bombing of noncombatants at Rotterdam and London, and subsequently there was dreadful retaliation on his own cities. Later Hitler diverted his resources to vengeance weapons, buzz bombs and rockets, which lost him command of the air over his vital transportation system.

Nevertheless, as we have seen, the Hitler rockets stimulated our own postwar development of guided missiles. Their possibilities, when combined with atomic explosives and our superior radar and electronic techniques, certainly suggest the concept of push-button warfare.

Of course, we should develop the most effective weapons our technology can supply, but until the now fantastic weapons of the future exist, push-button warfare is a dangerous concept on which to base current military posture. Even with the possession of radically new weapons, prudence counsels the retention and perfection of the old.

98

In general, the history of the introduction of new weapons, whether in the air, at sea, or on the ground, shows their more or less rapid incorporation into the military organization, which is gradually modified to absorb the innovation. The machine gun did not displace the rifle and bayonet, and the tank replaced only the horses of the cavalry. The dive bomber has not replaced artillery. Poison gas at one time threatened to frustrate the advance of an army, but its effects have never been sufficiently one sided to justify its use on a large scale.

Gloster Meteor (ground attack version) reported to carry four 1000-lb. bombs or 24 rockets, in addition to four 20-mm. cannon and wing-tip tanks. September 1951, Farnborough, England.

Guided missiles and pilotless aircraft promise a further enhancement of air power, both for attack and defense, and surely will become effective weapons in the future. The long-range bomber strengthens offensive air power too, while the supersonic interceptor-fighter strengthens air defense. As the new weapons are developed and become available for use, they can be integrated into the organizations of the Army, Navy and Air Force without premature scrapping of essential elements. Changes in strategy and tactical doctrine follow but do not anticipate the availability of new weapons.

Two Napalm strikes by B-26 bombers of Fifth Air Force on enemy railway near Wonsan, North Korea

Arguments about the use of tactical air power involve only the Defense Department, but the concept of intercontinental bombing involves the foreign policy of the United States in its efforts to implement mutual defense pacts. By these pacts we contemplate strongly holding friendly territory with land armies supported by tactical air power, with forward bases available from which to launch strategic air attacks into the interior of an enemy state. The need for intercontinental bombers should grow less as the United States' world position is consolidated by such alliances.

In the meantime the idea of being "liberated" by atomic bombs dropped by an intercontinental bombing strike is chilling to a potential ally. He may not wish to risk an alliance with this implication. And Britons, bombed in the last war, are reluctant to approve the use of atomic weapons by United States airplanes operated out of British bases. There has been an exchange in the House of Commons between Mr. Atlee and Mr. Churchill which leaves considerable doubt as to whether British sovereignty over British territory may not imply consultation or even a veto on United States strategic planning.

It is fortunate at this time of rapid technological change in weapons and growth of air power, that we have placed our Armed Services under a single Department of Defense. Such unification should ease the strains of adaptation. As new weapons and techniques make mass armies vulnerable, we may see a new kind of dispersed army of mechanized task forces with close air support and air supply. We have already seen how naval aviation has changed the battle order of the fleet into a complex of wide-ranging task forces built around airplane carriers.

I have left naval aviation out of this catalogue of the security aspects of air power until now because it includes all of them. Naval aviation is primarily the striking arm of sea power. The fast carrier task force is a mobile air base that can be quickly placed wherever required. It is complete with strategic, tactical and defense air elements, repair shops, spare parts, ammunition, stores and fuel supplies and a supply pipe line of a thousand ships reaching home. Other task forces of naval aviation patrol sea routes, escort and protect convoys, hunt down and kill submarines, and in general keep the sea communications open to our allies and our overseas commitments.

Under over-all war plans the Navy joins the Army and Air Force in support of major operations. This may, as in Korea, involve strikes from the carriers on shore targets and, as in the Western Pacific, air cover for landings of troops. The Navy bears, in effect, the nation's longest reaching air arm, as it may be quickly deployed in any sea without previous diplomatic negotiation, and without time-consuming arrangements for airbase construction and protection and the necessary logistic supply. It needs neither treaties nor permission.

Admiral William M. Fechteler, Chief of Naval Operations, has stated that: "Large attack-type aircraft of the most advanced type, and each capable of transporting nuclear weapons, are now operational from our Midway- and converted Essex-type carriers. The offensive potential of our carrier task forces has increased tremendously, and in fact, is still growing. The vast ocean spaces offer, to those who can command them, endless opportunities for

U.S.S. *Franklin D. Roosevelt* with airplane complement

swift, surprising attacks upon an enemy from many directions and with many weapons."[7] The admiral is undoubtedly mindful of Pearl Harbor and Manila where air strikes gained Japan in one day control of the South Pacific and its rich resources.

[7] "Naval Aviation Present and Future," *Sperryscope, 12,* No. 7, 1951, 7.

P2V Navy bomber making rocket-assisted take-off from flight deck of U.S.S. *Franklin D. Roosevelt*

Navy jet fighters Vought F7U (above) and Douglas F4D

Defense production is having a buoyant effect today on our national economy. The Air Force which has been building up toward 95 wings has extended its goal to 143 wings.[8] The presently authorized air program constitutes about half of total defense spending, and therefore any substantial increase in it can affect the whole defense setup, which in turn would affect the national economy.

The aircraft industry is straining to step up production but has already taken on about all it can handle. It is committed to triple production in 1952 in spite of manpower and material shortages. The leading aircraft builders are buried deep in orders. Engines, electronic gear, machine tools, and alloying elements like cobalt and columbium set a ceiling on production. Furthermore, the increasing complexity of today's weapons limits the practicability of boosting output by simple mass production. A mobile search radar set, for example, costs $782,798 and contains more than 500 vacuum tubes and 10 miles of circuits. It took 30 highly skilled engineering specialists two and one-half years to design it, and improvements are still being made. The air frame of the 1,500-horsepower Mustang fighter of the last war cost $14,000 but the 10,000-horsepower F-86 costs nearly $50,000. The F-86 required 27 times as much engineering manpower to design. When the F-86 is completely rigged out as an all-weather fighter with power plant, radar, guns, sights and spare parts the cost is about $625,000, or some 12 times the cost of the bare airplane. For such reasons actual production of combat aircraft in

8. *New York Times,* Dec. 11, 1951.

the next year or two cannot be much greater than the rate now planned.

However, defense spending can be stepped up for air bases and facilities at home and abroad, for naval carriers, and for training air and ground crews. A bomber pilot needs as long a training period as a doctor of philosophy.

We may expect air power spending to increase by billions and to be sustained at a high level even if no great war bursts upon us. This means a sort of simmering inflation as the defense boom is extended. If the Army and Navy should also get substantial increases, a broader segment of industry would be affected and shortages of civilian products would be marked.

There could eventually be some leveling off in defense spending from a new strategy using weapons now in the development stage. The possibility is seen, for use on targets in the ground battle area, of atomic weapons delivered by aircraft, guided missiles, and artillery. In this case we could assure our European allies of much greater striking power than had been hoped for. We could give the western world strength to offset Russia with smaller forces than are planned now. However, our program cannot be expected to change promptly because of new weapons, even when their performance is experimentally confirmed. In the short-range view it is likely that the incorporation of the new weapons into combat units will be superimposed on the present program. There is some truth in the statement that the stability of a long-range plan varies in direct proportion to the number of generals and bureaucrats who must initial any change.

We shall hear a great deal in the next few months about the necessity for strengthening the air power of the Atlantic nations. The net result will surely be a very substantial increase in the build-up of our own air power and increased aid to that of our allies. On any realistic appraisal of the world situation, we have no alternative.

First consideration will no doubt be given to the air defense of the United States against a crippling blow. The same threat to our allies by an enemy strategic air force gives us the responsibility to destroy it in its nest. This is a priority target for our Strategic Air Command. Furthermore, the importance of tactical air power in ground warfare is now so great that the United Nations must have a tactical air force in Europe capable of quickly seizing command of the air. The fewer divisions we have, the more air groups we need. Consequently, there are strong grounds for an accelerated build-up of tactical air power in Europe and also of a reserve at home for possible action in other parts of the world.

The future was never less clear than now, but while the cold war continues this country will arm itself. However, we can overdo it. We could embark on a production program so ambitious as to exhaust our economy by the accumulation of great stocks of present-day aircraft that may too soon become obsolete. We may lack the resources or the will to replace this stockpile. Research and development must proceed with vigor and imagination as insurance against the risk of such a calamity. During the indefinite period of international strain there must be a nice balance in the current effort devoted to the various elements of air power and to a program of research and development. It is true that research tends to accelerate the obsolescence both of our own present equipment, and our enemy's. But under adequate security cover the expec-

Avro 707B, a British delta-wing jet-propelled research airplane

tation is that our own industry can apply results of research to create aircraft in a series of always superior models.

Probably the capabilities of our air power in being should be widely advertised while the objectives and results of research and development should be secret. Such a policy is difficult to apply, however, since scientific research flourishes best with free and open discussion of its problems. The present practice is to publish theoretical research

Boeing B-47 bomber in its first rocket-assisted take-off test. Smoke trails are made

in aeronautical science but to withhold military applications. There is always the danger that almost any research might be declared to have some remote future military value and hence be locked up to wither in a secret archive. While we may feel that some stupid things are done in the name of security, the really stupid, the grossly stupid thing, is the envy and malice of the Communist powers. So long as they threaten us, scientists and engineers must accept restriction in the full exercise of their professional ideal of service to society.

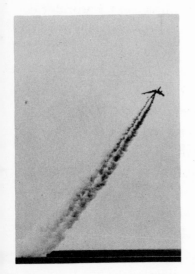 

by 18 rocket units and six jet engines giving a combined thrust of 42,000 lbs.

INTERNATIONAL SOCIETY

Western society in the past has survived long periods of almost continuous warfare. With the building of roads war spread over a more extended area; and eventually nations succeeded robber barons and city states. Ocean-going ships carried conquest overseas, and colonies were established which have since evolved into great states. Aeronautics, the new tool of global transportation, offers new means to make war at a distance. By this very threat it stimulates efforts to seek voluntary adjustments between nations in order to resolve their fears of one another.

Aeronautics can be a tool to implement a world-wide regime of law and order. It facilitates the meetings of statesmen, the conduct of inspections and police action, and in general can serve for both surveillance and enforcement. In our future, whether it be a time of peace or of war, aeronautics is sure to be a dominant activity. The airplane was born in the United States and has been carried to its highest state of development here. The United States has strong reasons to lead in its application to the defense of that part of the world pledged to mutual cooperation.

Social effects of a great discovery or invention ordinarily are expected to evolve rather slowly with increased use. Our generation has been subject to the convergence of two astounding manifestations of technology, the airplane and atomic energy. These discoveries are likened by Professor Urey to the wheel and to fire, with nothing comparable in social implications since the Ice Age.[9] This combined social effect is already apparent in international relations. Air power has immensely increased the national power of large industrialized states at the expense of smaller ones. Since the second World War two great powers have become superpowers, seeking affiliations with nearby weaker states. The political world has become bipolar, with a dual pattern of security zones made up of tiers of friendly states.[10] The

[9] Harold C. Urey, "Atomic Energy, Aviation, and Society," *Air Affairs*, Sept. 1946, p. 22.

[10] William Fielding Ogburn, "Aviation and International Relations," *Air Affairs*, Dec. 1949, pp. 522-538.

offensive potentiality of air power creates an urge to establish an even wider circle of security, but advancing technology makes the desired circles of security intersect. The bipolar pattern of security is only an illusion; it really presents zones of friction and cold war.

While this pattern persists we may expect to see, as derivative effects, an increase in the power differential in favor of the great states and a consequent integration of smaller states into their economic and cultural orbits. Such an unequal relation between states makes for a forced marriage, influenced by air power as the shotgun, and by civil aeronautics to make it convenient. Civil aeronautics makes for easy interlocking of business enterprises and peaceful penetration by way of publications, trade, and visitors. Central control and uniformity of public administration follow. In so far as the small states seek security in return for allegiance, the process resembles feudalism.

Professor Ogburn[11] has said that historians are reluctant to give credit to technology rather than to great men as a social force, while philosophers of history give all credit to ideas. Columbus did discover America and set in train a vast succession of social changes, but back of Columbus lay the development of the ship. Without Columbus some other European would have discovered the New World; the existence of the ship guaranteed it.

There is a propelling force in technology which drives great men and also constitutes the propelling force of ideas. For example, the force of nationalism which is powerful today is really an adaptation to conditions created by technology. The territorial base for the modern state was laid

11. *Loc. cit.*

by inventions in transportation and consolidated by communications. Without these nationalism would be restricted to a very small area. Finally the present international struggle, which is accentuated nationalism, is based on the inventions of warfare, principally air power. Technology prepares the way for statesmen or for conquerors.

History gives ample grounds to expect that aeronautics will be a great force in the evolution of society. The railroad has already contributed to urbanizing our life, consolidating our territory, increasing the specialization of labor, and has furthered mass production and the breakup of household economy. The automobile has made great changes in our cities and farms, our family life, and also in crime, morals, and manners. The airplane, by the principle of continuity of trends, should do something more along the same lines and, in addition, produce other effects on our society that are as yet unpredictable.

There is a huge disproportion between human wisdom and human power. Perhaps the best fruits of knowledge are tools, yet the steamship can be a battleship. The airplane of the gentle Wright brothers has become the vehicle for a world-wide system of air transportation and, at the same time, the means for the annihilation of cities. There have been sermons on the good and evil of new knowledge, and the dedicated research man is not unaware of the perils of his success. The airplane is just another tool to serve the purposes of mankind, whether for good or evil is determined by the user. The individual with an airplane is not a serious menace as he is controlled by the police power of the state. So is the individual with a torch or a motorcar. The whole apparatus of air power, however, is a tool of the state, to be used as its leaders may desire. In them we must hope for wisdom.

Complex societies are expected to produce social patterns capable of absorbing innovations. Our present international society is in the process of adjusting itself to the innovation of flight with space no longer hampering the free communication of ideas and the interchange of goods and people. The adjustment is painful, and the final pattern has not yet evolved.

According to Alfred Whitehead, "Those organisms are successful which modify their environments so as to assist each other. . . . A forest is the triumph of the organization of mutually dependent species. . . . There is something in the ready use of force which defeats its own object. Its main defect is that it bars cooperation. Every organism requires an environment of friends, partly to shield it from violent changes, and partly to supply it with its wants."[12]

In scientific research we have a self-evolving system like a chain reaction. Research produces new knowledge whose applications confront us with new problems. These problems in turn excite new research with further new and perhaps unexpected results. The evolution of aeronautics has proceeded in this way on a wide front, and we may expect it to continue at an even more rapid rate.

Research presses against the apparent limitations to further progress. At any given time the limitations appear to be formidable because our knowledge is limited. But we can be sure that aeronautical research and engineering development will continue both to extend our knowledge and to apply it in new ways.

The final half of this century will disclose the use that

[12.] *Science and the Modern World*, pp. 296, 297.

society makes of the mobility gained by the conquest of the air. Progress in aeronautics is proceeding with vast momentum. In this country alone expenditures on aeronautical research and development for this year and next will total more than $1 billion. Dollars alone do not guarantee technical advances, but the national effort measured by these appropriations means a heavy diversion of scientific, engineering, and industrial manpower to the advancement of aeronautics.

One may well expect that the results of world-wide efforts will in time be substantial, with consequent disturbance of the relatively static distribution of man and his works over the earth as determined primarily by physical geography. Charles Seymour in his Bowman Memorial Lecture predicts that the ultimate adjustment of conflicting political interests "must be founded upon an intelligent understanding of human geography . . . of the natural barriers and communications which divide or unite."[13] Such ultimate adjustment must of necessity include patterns of political, economic, and community life consistent with the power to use a third dimension of geography.

[13.] American Geographical Society, New York, 1951.

THE TERRY LECTURES

Volumes Published by the Yale University Press
on the Dwight Harrington Terry Foundation